Table of Contents

Module 1 1
Module 2 12
Module 3 22
Module 4 34
Module 5 44
Module 6 58
Module 7 69
Module 8 81
Module 9 92
Module 10 104
Module 11 115
Module 12 130
Module 13 137
Module 14 145
Module 15 152
Module 16 160
Module 17 168
Module 18 175
Cutout Worksheets 184
Extra Resources 244

This workbook contains all of the worksheets found in the Math 3 Semester A course. To see the worksheet in color, view it online within the lessons. For any worksheets containing cutting activities, they can be found in the "Cutout Worksheets" section. The "Extra Resources" contain helpful tools that students are learning to use.

© 2022 by Accelerate Education
Visit us on the Web at www.accelerate.education

Name: _____ Date: _____

Match and Multiply!

Draw a line to match each strategy with the correct multiplication sentence. Then use the strategy to find each product!

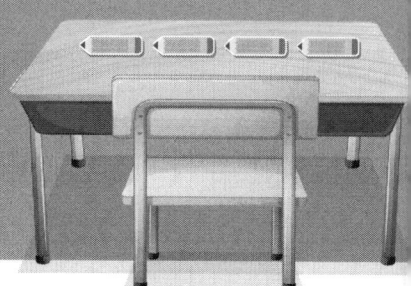

Example:

2 x 3 = 6

1. 3 + 3 + 3 + 3 = ? •   • 3 x 3 =

2.   •   • 4 x 3 =

3.   •   • 3 x 5 =

4. 5, 10, 15   •   • 5 x 4 =

1

1.1 Equal Groups: Multiplication

Name: _____ Date: _____

Fill It In!

Parts of each problem are missing! Fill in the:
- Multiplication picture with the correct number of dots.
- Repeated addition sentence with the correct repeated addends.
- Multiplication sentence with the correct factors.

Then find the sum and product!

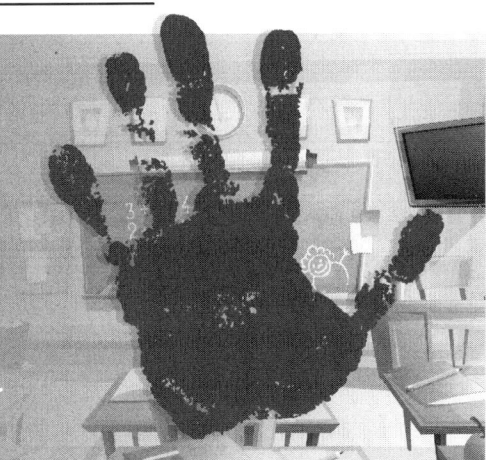

Example:

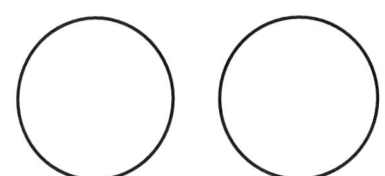

$\underline{4} + \underline{4} = \underline{8}$

$\underline{2} \times \underline{4} = \underline{8}$

1.

$3 + 3 = \underline{}$

$2 \times 3 = \underline{}$

2.

$2 + 2 + 2 + 2 + 2 = \underline{}$

$\underline{} \times \underline{} = \underline{}$

1.2 Multiplication as Repeated Addition

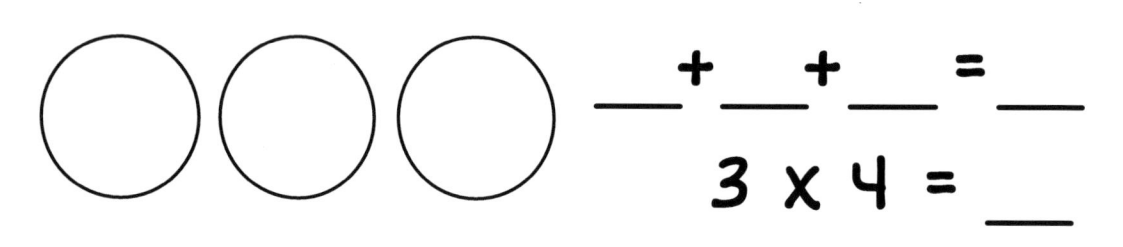

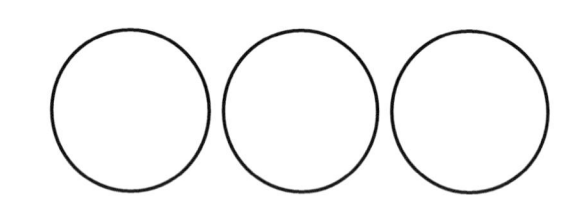

3.

○ ○ ○   ___ + ___ + ___ = ___

3 x 4 = ___

4.

○ ○ ○   5 + 5 + 5 = ___

3 x 5 = ___

5.

○ ○ ○ ○ ○   4 + 4 + 4 + 4 + 4 = ___

___ x ___ = ___

Name: _____ Date: _____

Color and Multiply!
Use what you know about multiplying with number lines to create multiplication sentences.

Look at the number lines. Find the one that shows correct jumping and totals. Lightly color it in with a crayon. Use the correct number line to write and solve a multiplication sentence.

Example:

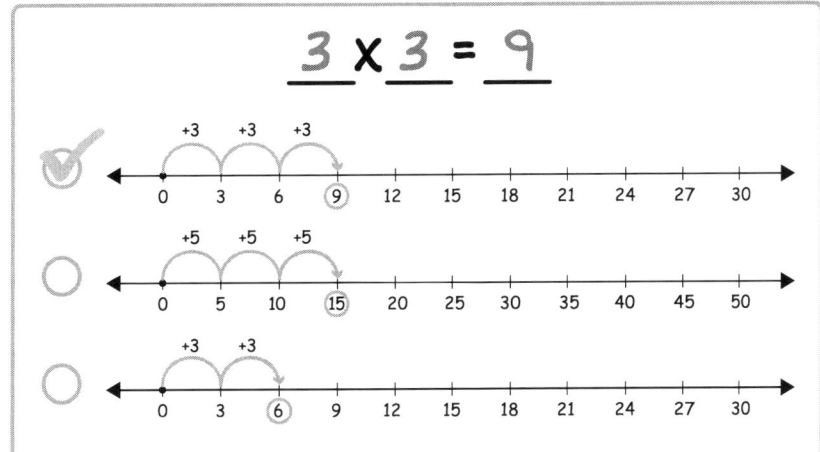

1.

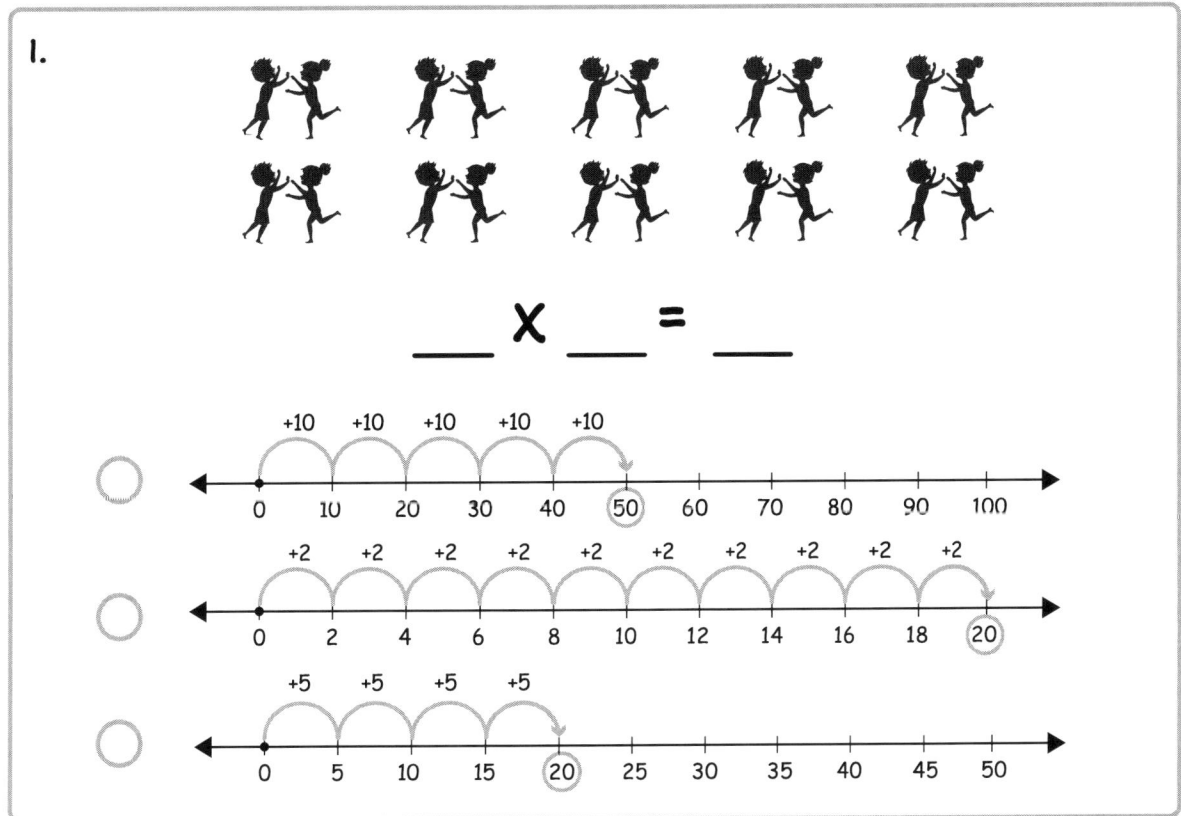

__ X __ = __

1.4 Using a Number Line to Multiply

2.

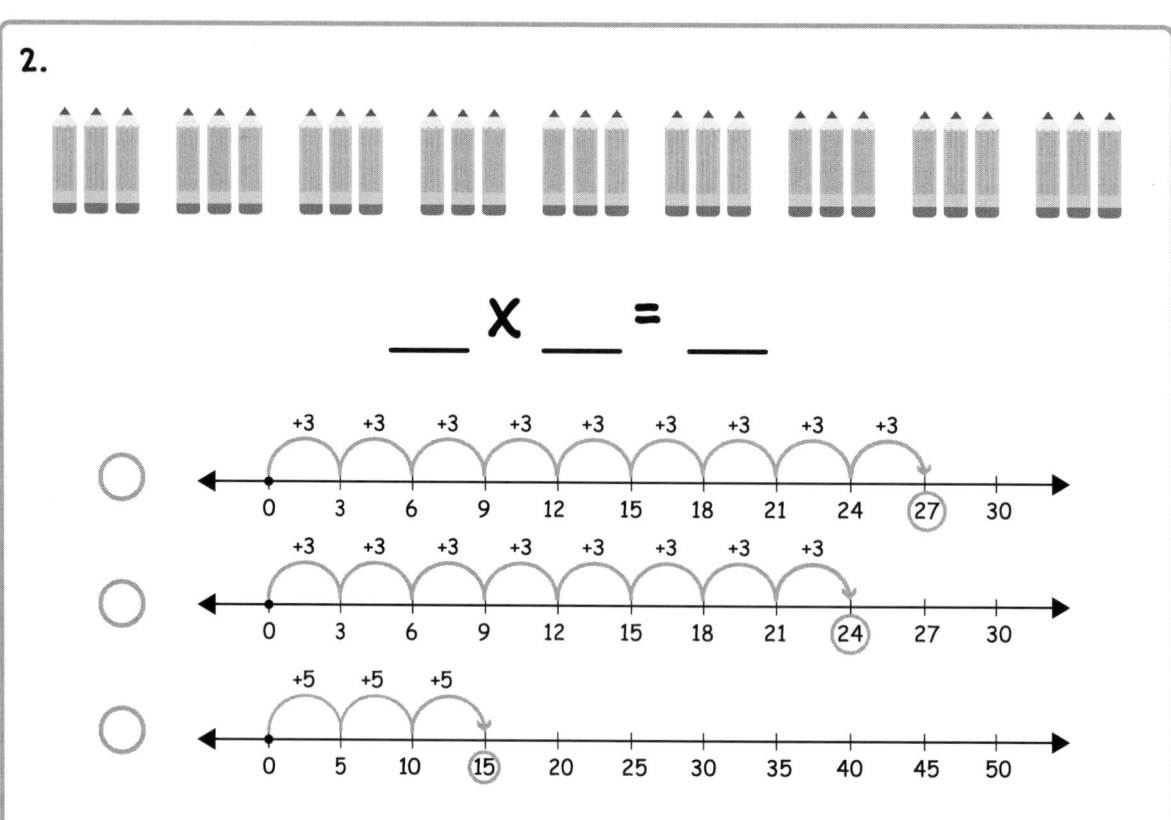

3.

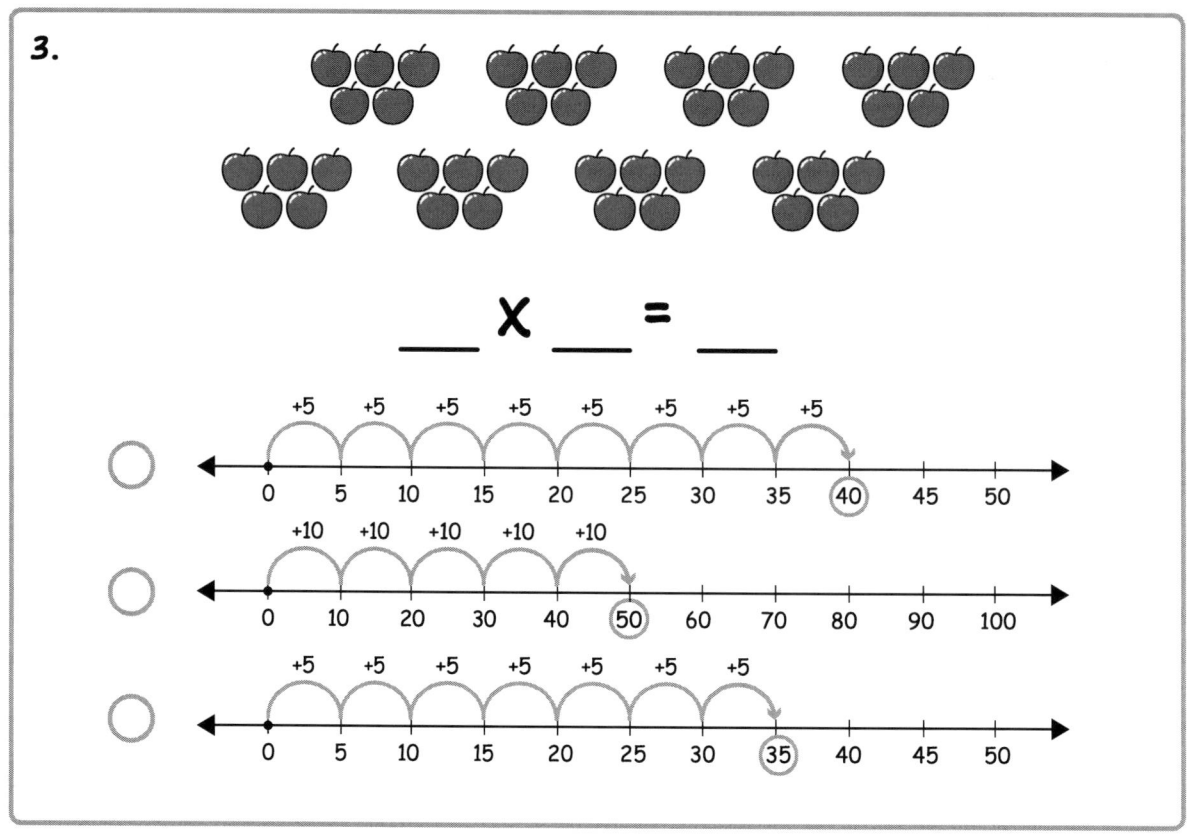

1.4 Using a Number Line to Multiply

4.

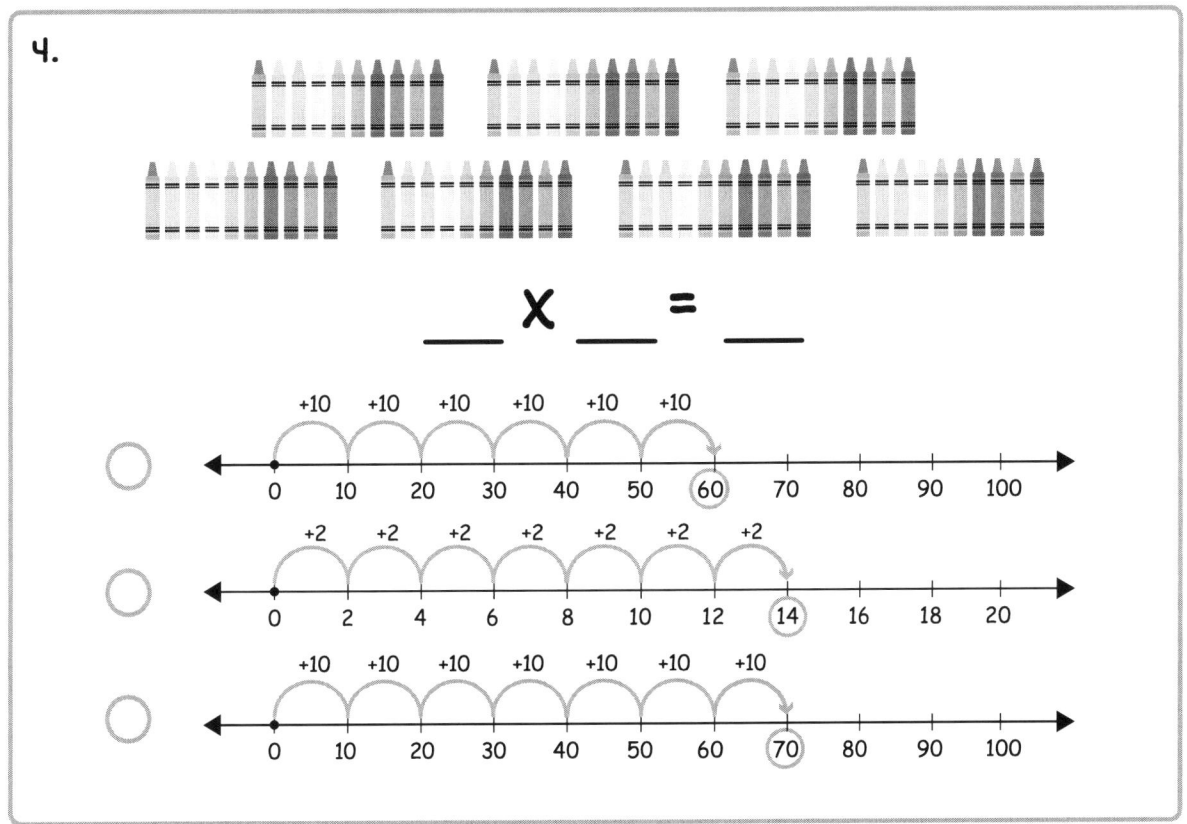

___ x ___ = ___

5. Try it Out! Use the multiplication sentence to find the number of jumps. Draw the jumps with your crayon on the number line and circle the answer.

6 x 10 = 60

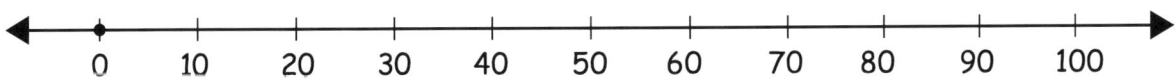

1.4 Using a Number Line to Multiply

Name: _____ Date: _____

Read, Choose, Multiply!

Read each problem. Find the important information. Choose one strategy and use it to find the answer with a blue marker. Write the answer on the line with the label word.

Example:

Ava made **4** cards. She drew 3 flowers on (each) card. <u>How many flowers did she draw?</u>

$$4 \times 3 = ?$$

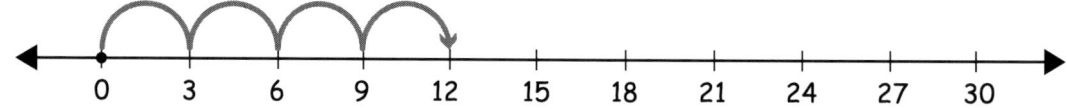

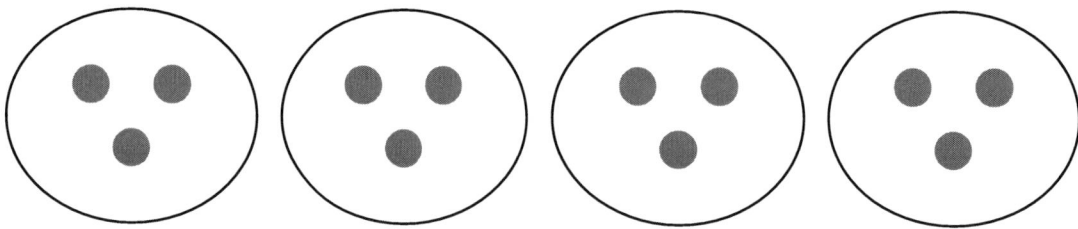

_3_, _6_, _9_, _12_

_3_ + _3_ + _3_ + _3_ = ?

12 flowers

7   1.5 Problem Solving: Using Multiplication Strategies

Next page

1. Ava made 4 cards. She drew 4 leaves on each card. <u>How many leaves did she draw?</u>

4 x 4 = ?

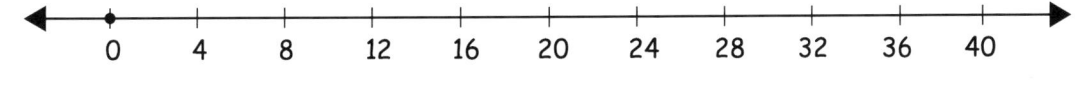

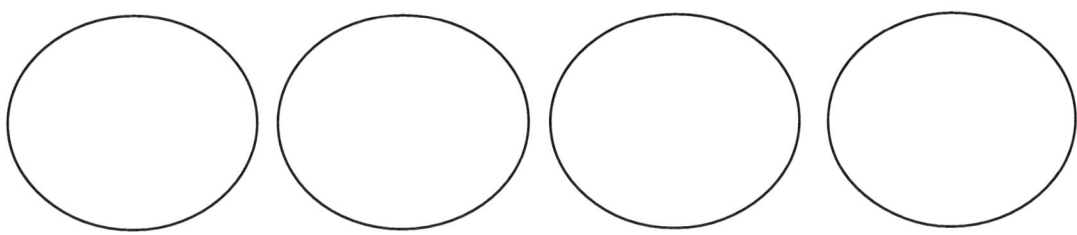

1.5 Problem Solving: Using Multiplication Strategies

2. Ava made 6 cards with 5 zoo animals per card. <u>How many zoo animals did she draw?</u>

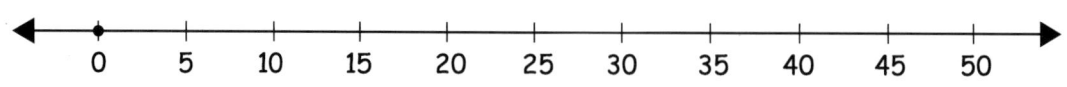

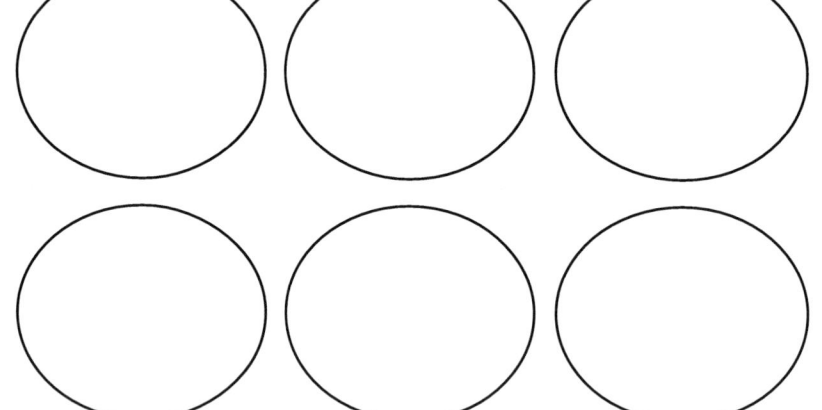

__ , __ , __ , __ , __ , __

__ + __ + __ + __ + __ + __ = ?

3. Ava has 9 piles of cards. There are 2 flowers on each card. <u>How many flowers are on Ava's cards?</u>

$$9 \times 2 = ?$$

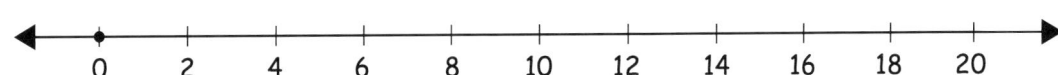

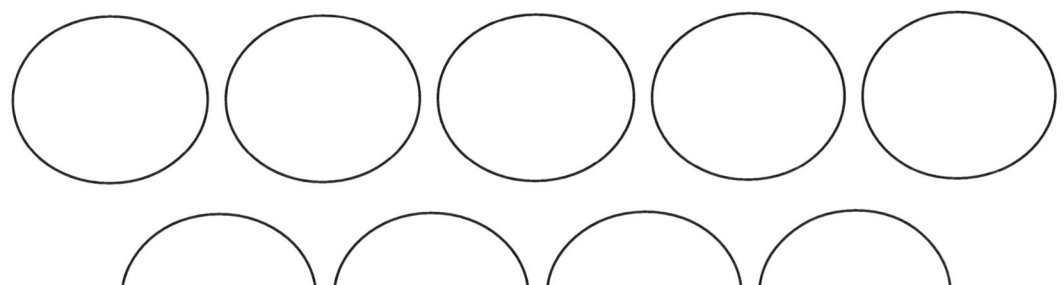

__,__,__,__,__,__,__,__,__

__+__+__+__+__+__+__+__+__ = ?

1.5 Problem Solving: Using Multiplication Strategies

4. Ava drew 8 groups of 3 cats. How many cats did she draw?

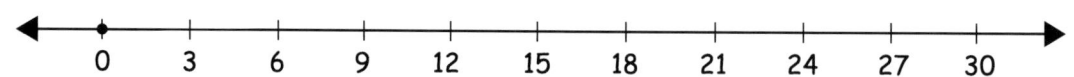

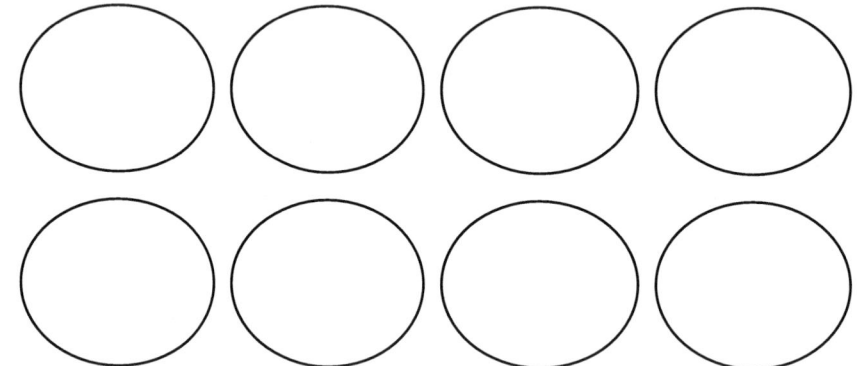

__ , __ , __ , __ , __ , __ , __ , __

__ + __ + __ + __ + __ + __ + __ + __ = ?

Name: _____ Date: _____

Circle, Write, Multiply!
Use multiplication pictures and expressions to create an equation.

Look at the picture. Circle the expression that matches the picture. Then write it on the line. Turn it into an equation to solve!

Example:

5 x 6 = 30

7 x 4   (5 x 6)   5 x 5

1.

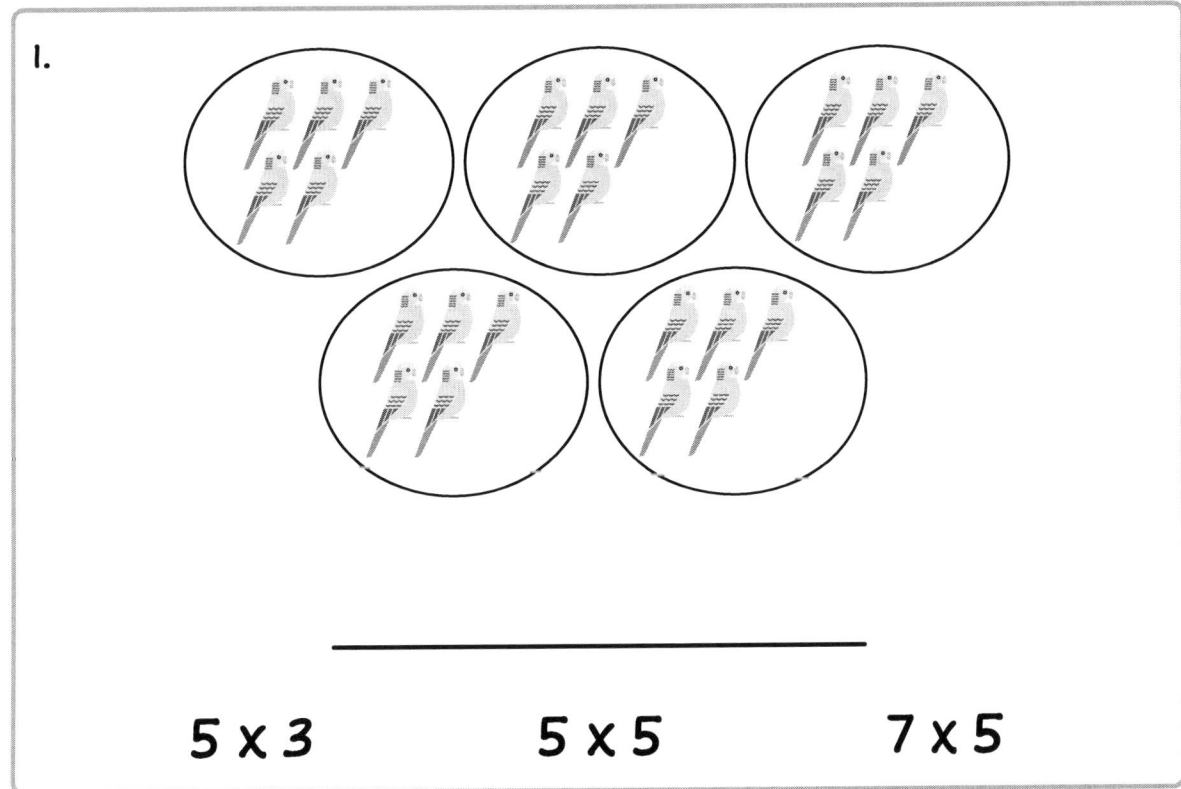

_____

5 x 3   5 x 5   7 x 5

2.1 Multiplication Expressions and Equations

2.

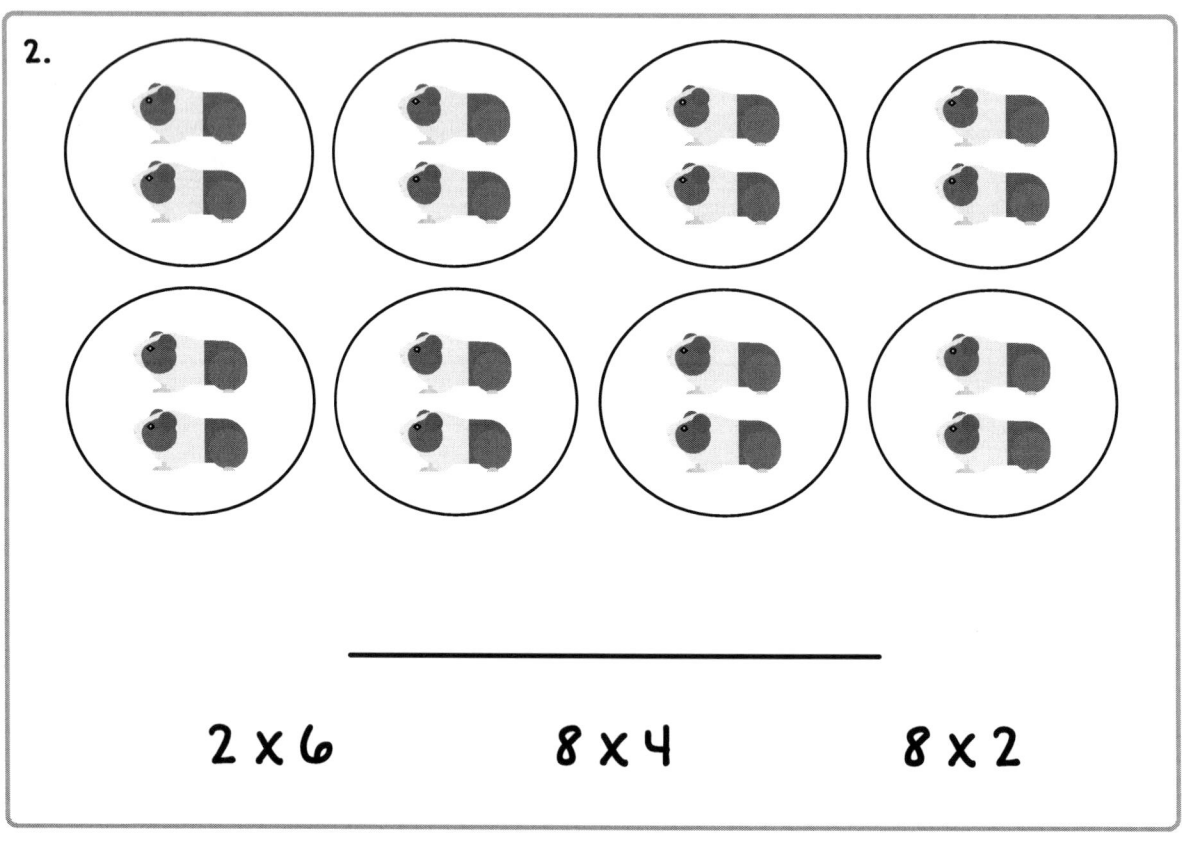

2 x 6   8 x 4   8 x 2

3.

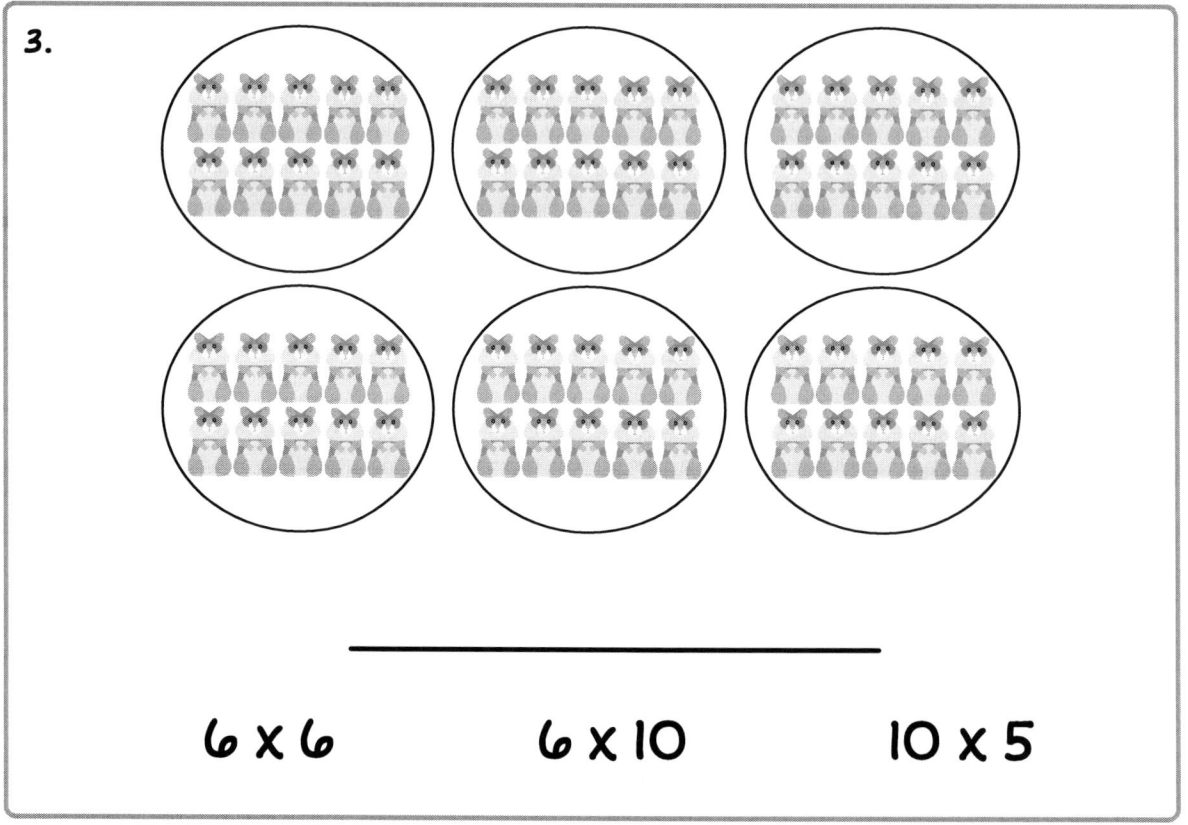

6 x 6   6 x 10   10 x 5

2.1 Multiplication Expressions and Equations

4.

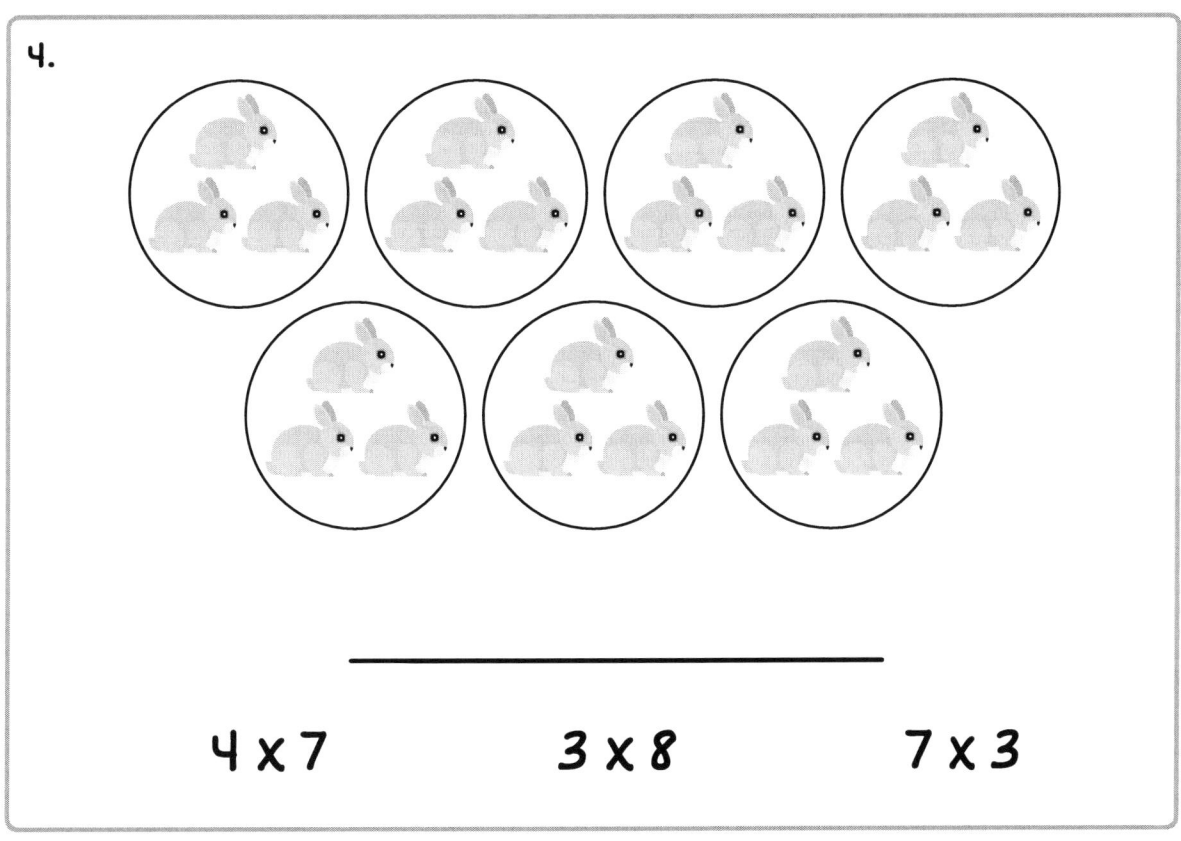

4 x 7   3 x 8   7 x 3

5.

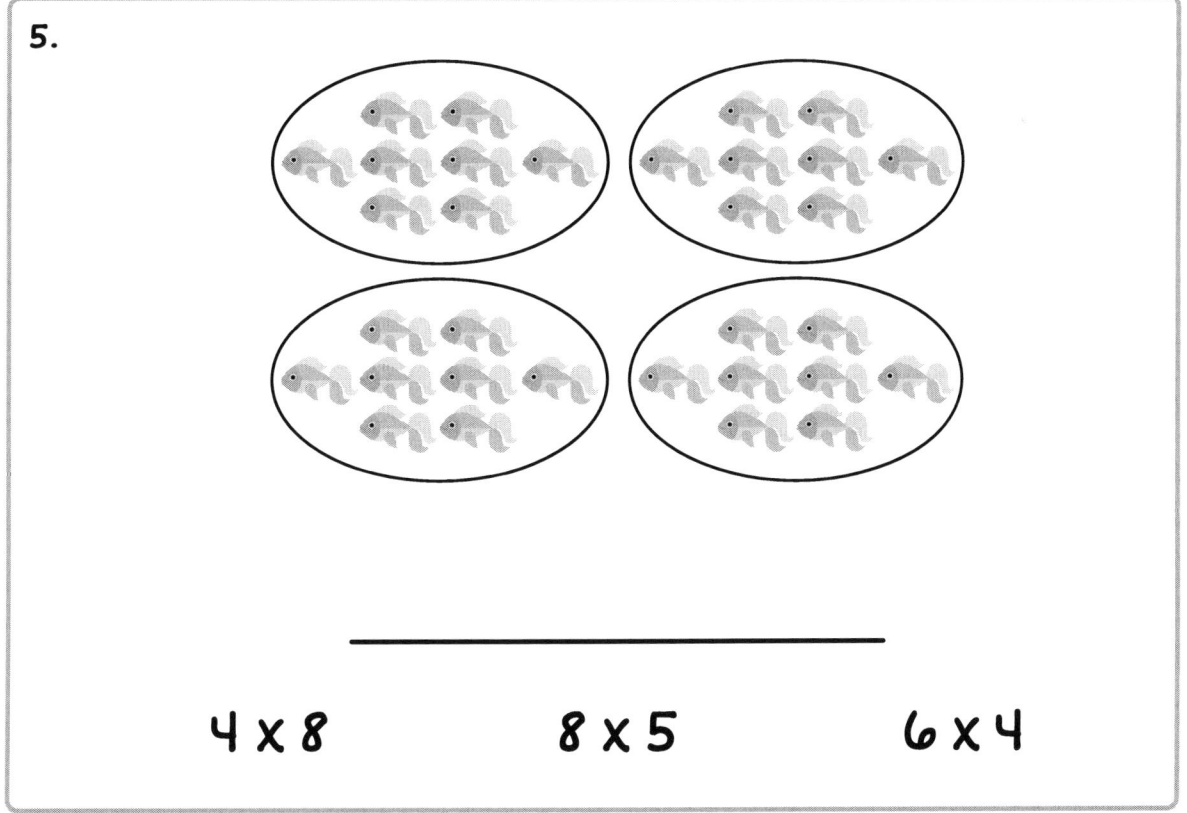

4 x 8   8 x 5   6 x 4

2.1 Multiplication Expressions and Equations

Name: _____ Date: _____

Color, Match, Multiply!
Use what you know about arrays and multiplication to answer the questions below.

1. Draw an array to show each expression. Then, fill in the answer.

a. 7 x 2 = ___

b. 4 x 9 = ___

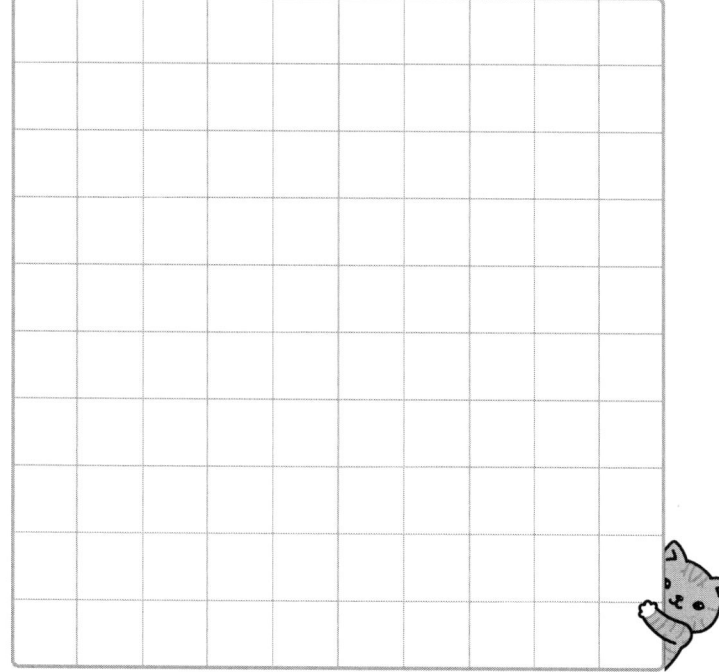

2. Use your marker to fill in each square with any shape. Match the array to the correct equation. Then use the array to find the product!

Example: 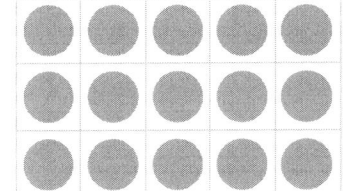 —————• $3 \times 5 = \underline{15}$

 • • $5 \times 4 = \underline{}$

 • • $7 \times 5 = \underline{}$

 • • $2 \times 8 = \underline{}$

 • • $4 \times 7 = \underline{}$

2.3 Using Arrays to Multiply

Name: _____ Date: _____

Multiply and Color!

Use what you know about a multiplication chart to help Marley get home!

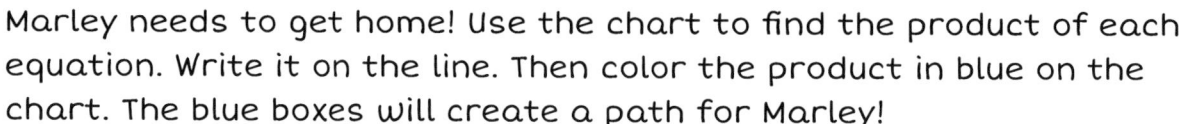

Marley needs to get home! Use the chart to find the product of each equation. Write it on the line. Then color the product in blue on the chart. The blue boxes will create a path for Marley!

X	1	2	3	4	5	6	7	8	9	10
1	1	2	3	4	5	6	7	8	9	10
2	2	4	6	8	10	12	14	16	18	20
3	3	6	9	12	15	18	21	24	27	30
4	4	8	12	16	20	24	28	32	36	40
5	5	10	15	20	25	30	35	40	45	50
6	6	12	18	24	30	36	42	48	54	60
7	7	14	21	28	35	42	49	56	63	70
8	8	16	24	32	40	48	56	64	72	80
9	9	18	27	36	45	54	63	72	81	90
10	10	20	30	40	50	60	70	80	90	100

1. 10 x 3 = ___ 2. 9 x 4 = ___ 3. 8 x 4 = ___ 4. 7 x 5 = ___

5. 6 x 6 = ___ 6. 7 x 7 = ___ 7. 8 x 7 = ___ 8. 9 x 8 = ___

9. 9 x 9 = ___ 10. 10 x 10 = ___

Name: _____ Date: _____

Read, Choose, Multiply!

Use what you know about multiplication strategies to solve problems.

Read each problem. Find the important information. Choose a strategy to solve the problem. Write the answer on the line with the label word.

Example:

The third grade students helped 6 groups of 3 dogs. <u>How many dogs did they help (in all)?</u>

$6 \times 3 = ?$

Choose one to solve the problem

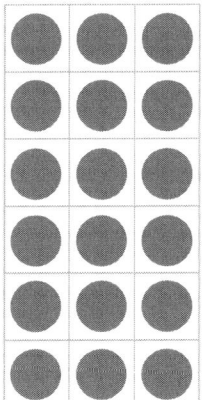
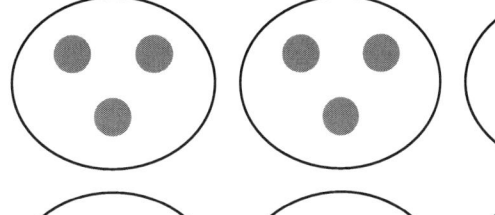

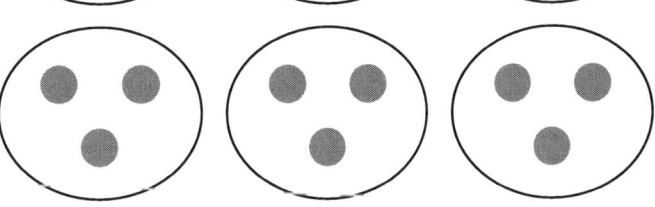
18 dogs

2.5 Problem Solving: Applying Multiplication Strategies

18
Next page

1. The third grade students helped 5 groups of 4 cats. How many cats did they help in all?

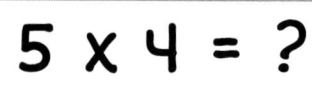

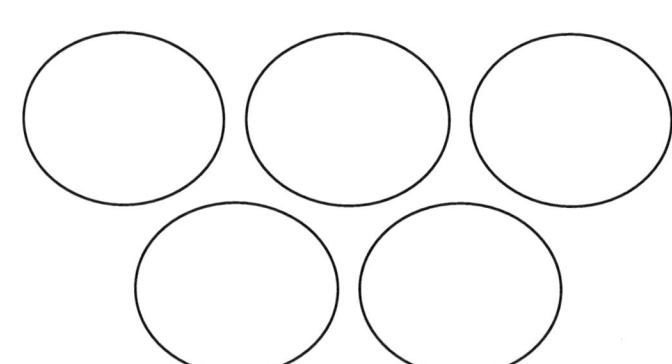

2. The third grade students helped 6 groups of 6 dogs. How many dogs did they help in total?

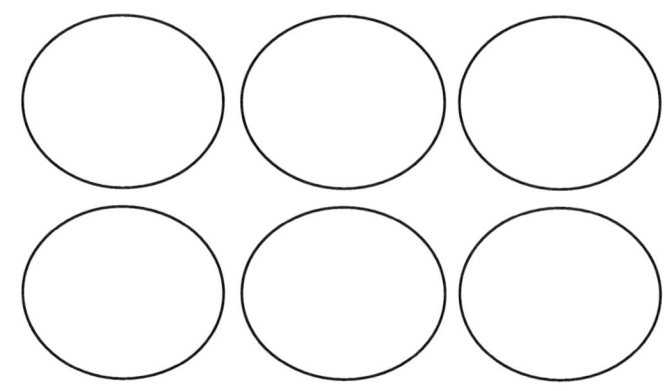

19   2.5 Problem Solving: Applying Multiplication Strategies

Next page

3. The third grade students helped 7 groups of 5 cats. How many cats did they help in all?

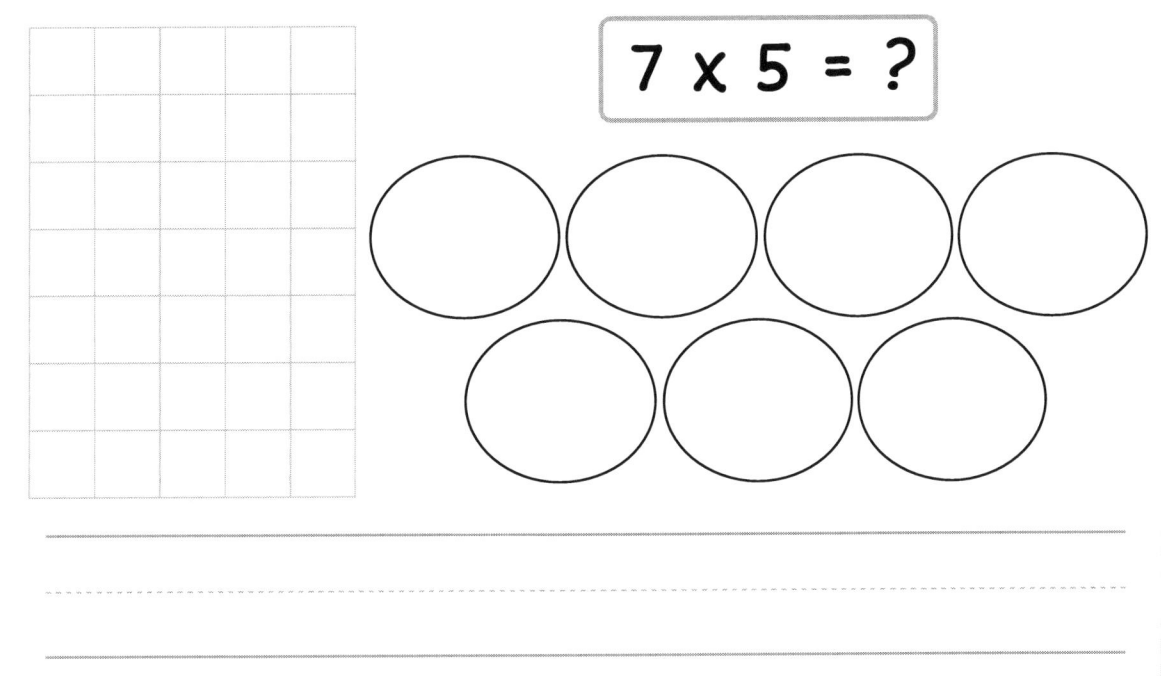

4. The third grade students helped 6 groups of 7 dogs. How many dogs did they help in total?

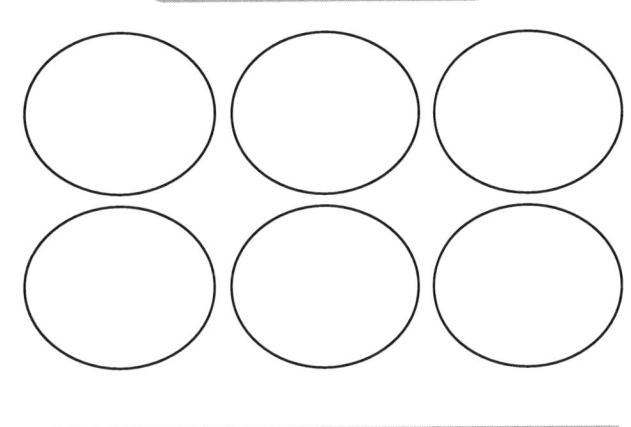

2.5 Problem Solving: Applying Multiplication Strategies

Now check your work! Use the multiplication chart to check your answers.

X	1	2	3	4	5	6	7	8	9	10
1	1	2	3	4	5	6	7	8	9	10
2	2	4	6	8	10	12	14	16	18	20
3	3	6	9	12	15	18	21	24	27	30
4	4	8	12	16	20	24	28	32	36	40
5	5	10	15	20	25	30	35	40	45	50
6	6	12	18	24	30	36	42	48	54	60
7	7	14	21	28	35	42	49	56	63	70
8	8	16	24	32	40	48	56	64	72	80
9	9	18	27	36	45	54	63	72	81	90
10	10	20	30	40	50	60	70	80	90	100

Name: _____ Date: _____

Trace and Divide!
Complete the problems below using division by equal groups.

Get 30 pieces of cereal. Use the correct amount to make equal groups. Draw a circle underneath the pieces of cereal in each group. Then use the picture you made to find the quotient!

Example:

There are 8 pieces of cereal. Put them into 2 equal groups.

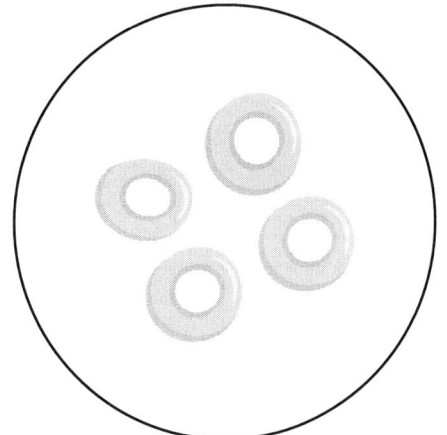
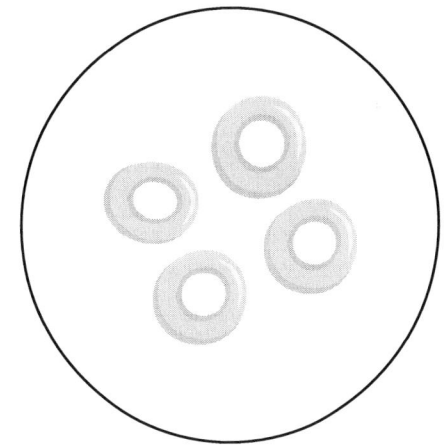

$8 \div 2 = \underline{4}$

3.1 Using Equal Groups to Divide

1. There are 9 pieces of cereal. Put them into 3 equal groups.

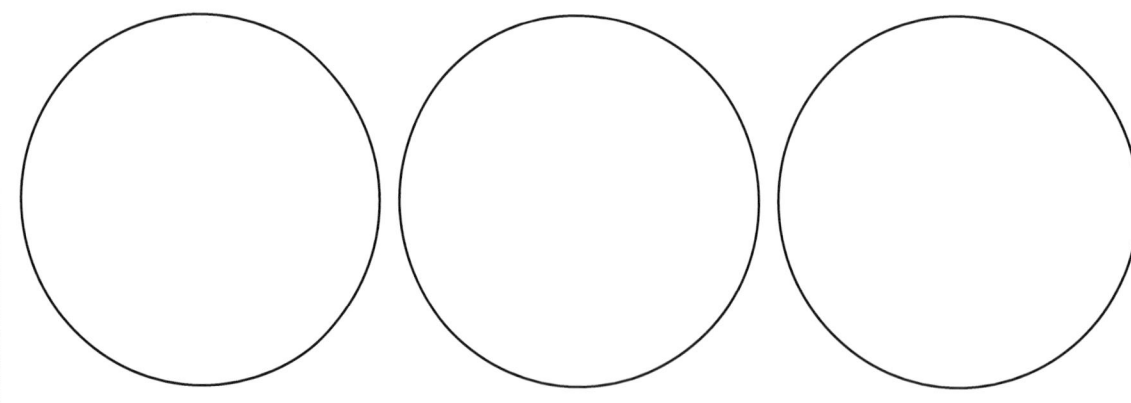

9 ÷ 3 = ___

2. There are 12 pieces of cereal. Put them into 2 equal groups.

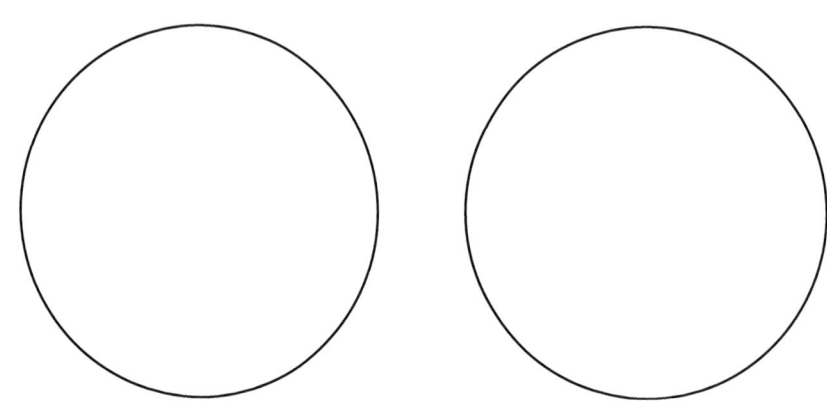

12 ÷ 2 = ___

3. There are 24 pieces of cereal. Put them into 8 equal groups.

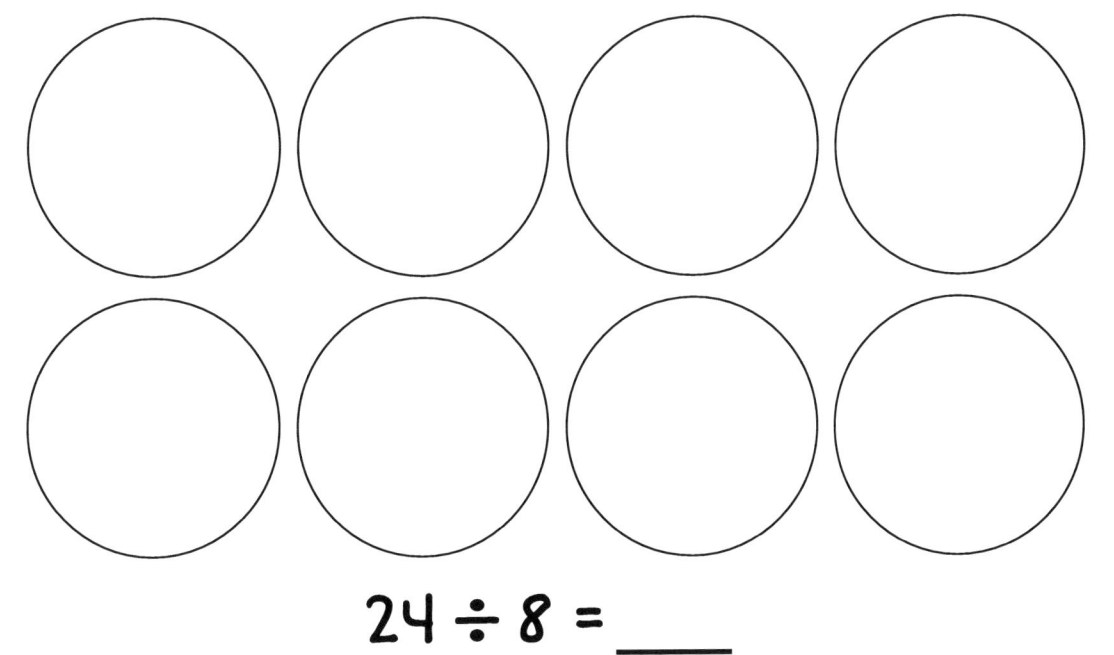

24 ÷ 8 = ___

4. There are 18 pieces of cereal. Put them into 9 equal groups.

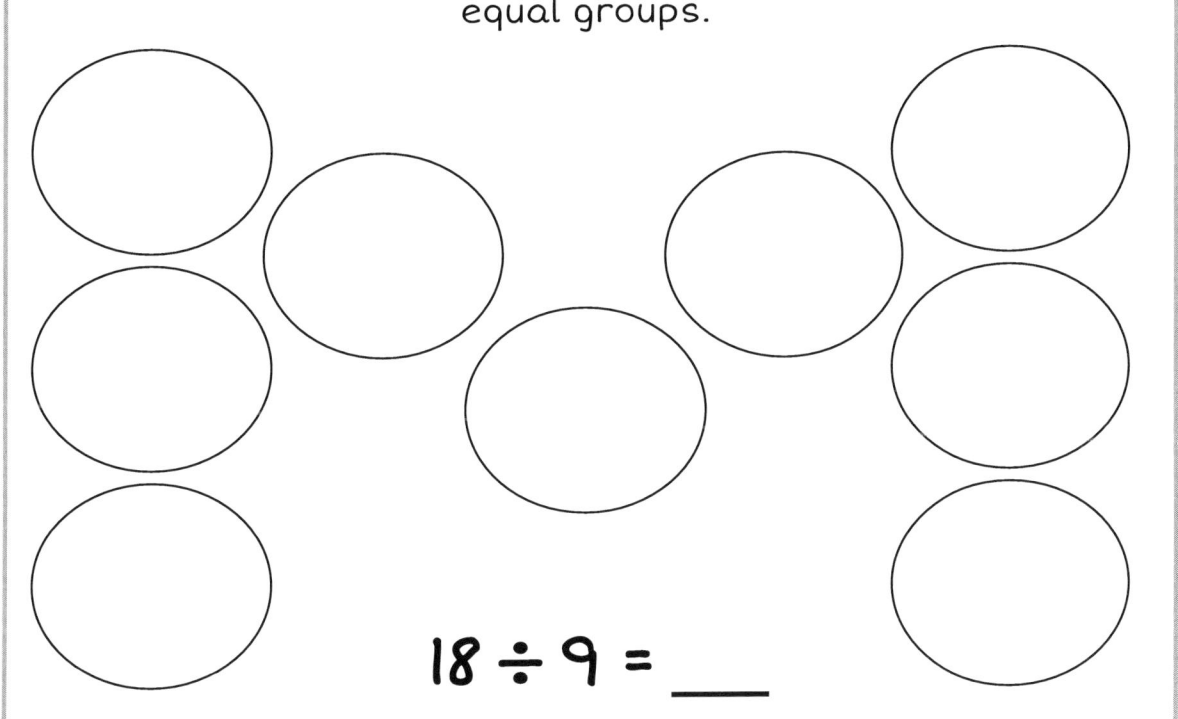

18 ÷ 9 = ___

3.1 Using Equal Groups to Divide

Name: _____ Date: _____

Move It Away!

Use your counters to solve each division problem below using repeated subtraction.

Read each problem. Put the correct number of counters in the box. Then take away equal groups to match the repeated subtraction sentence. Count the groups you take out to find the quotient! Write each quotient on the line.

Example:

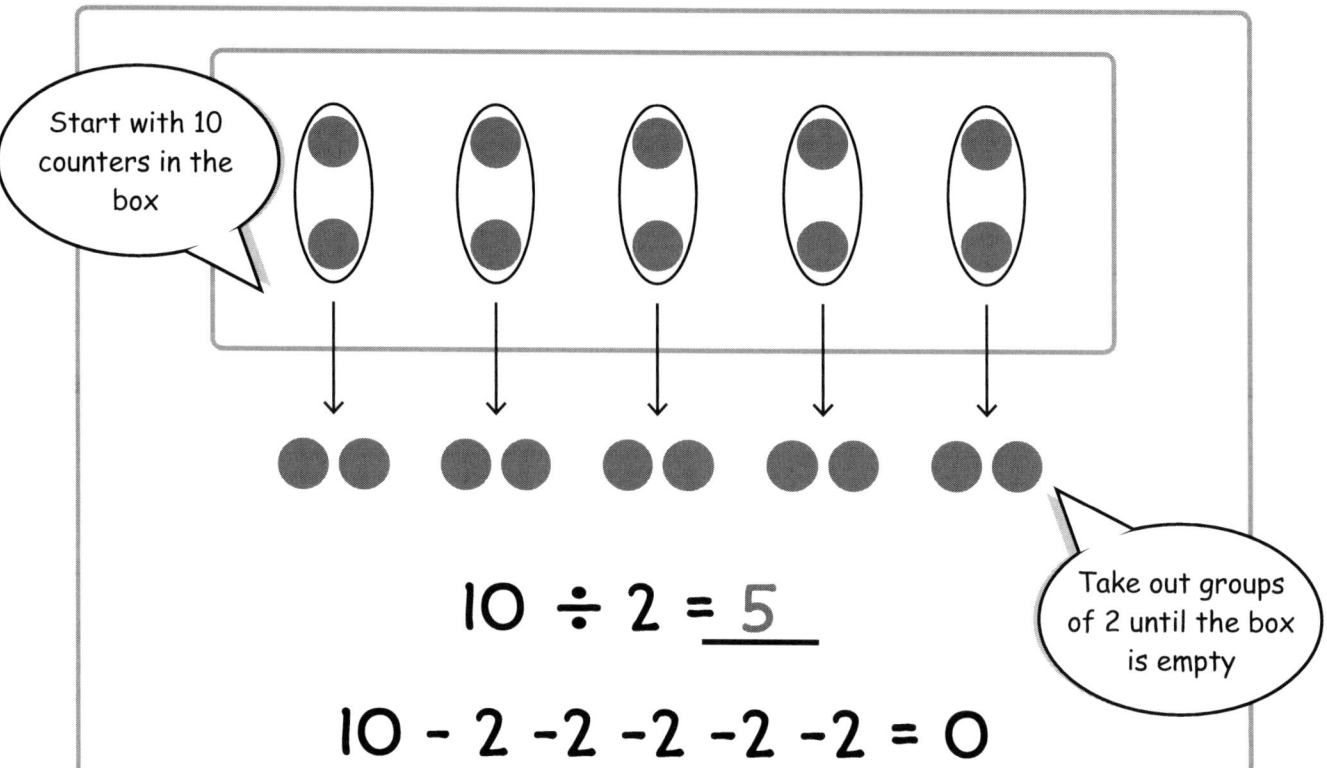

3.2 Division as Repeated Subtraction

Next page

1.

$12 \div 6 = $ ___

$12 - 6 - 6 = 0$

2.

$18 \div 6 = $ ___

$18 - 6 - 6 - 6 = 0$

3.2 Division as Repeated Subtraction

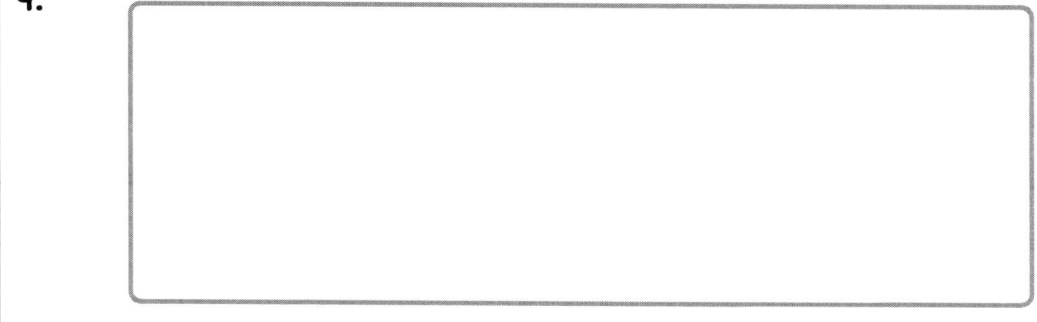

3.

$25 \div 5 = \underline{}$

$25 - 5 - 5 - 5 - 5 - 5 = 0$

4.

$30 \div 5 = \underline{}$

$30 - 5 - 5 - 5 - 5 - 5 - 5 = 0$

3.2 Division as Repeated Subtraction

5.

$40 \div 4 = $ ___

$40 - 4 - 4 - 4 - 4 - 4 - 4 - 4 - 4 - 4 - 4 = 0$

3.2 Division as Repeated Subtraction

Name: _____ Date: _____

Color, Multiply, Divide!
Use what you know about arrays, multiplication, and division to complete the questions below.

Create an array by filling in the correct number of rows and columns. Use the array to find the product of the multiplication sentence. Then use the array to find the quotient of the division sentence. Write both on the lines.

Example:

6 x 6 = 36

36 ÷ 6 = 6

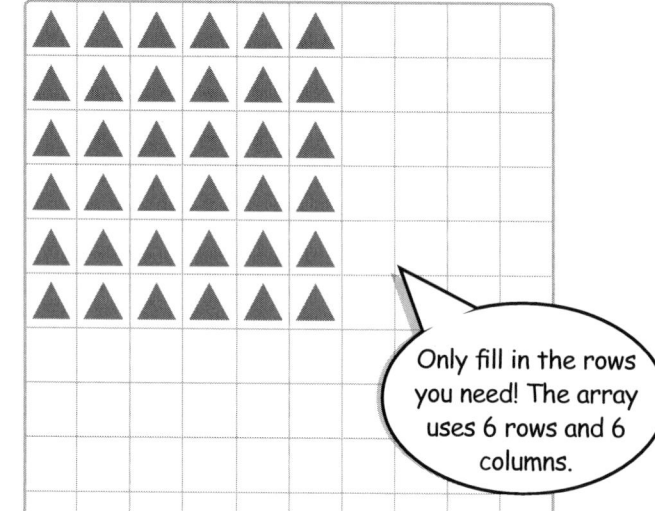

Remember: The total number of shapes is the product. The number of shapes in a row is the quotient

Only fill in the rows you need! The array uses 6 rows and 6 columns.

1. 4 x 8 = ___

   32 ÷ 4 = ___

29

3.4 Use Arrays to Relate Multiplication and Division

2. 5 × 9 = ___

   45 ÷ 5 = ___

3. 9 × 7 = ___

   63 ÷ 9 = ___

3.4 Use Arrays to Relate Multiplication and Division

Name: _____   Date: _____

Look and Write!
Use division strategies to write division sentences.

Look at each division strategy. Use it to find the dividend, divisor, and quotient. Write them on the correct lines!

Example:

$\underline{20} \div \underline{4} = \underline{5}$

1.

___ ÷ ___ = ___

31   3.5 Applying Division Strategies

Next page

2. ___ ÷ ___ = ___

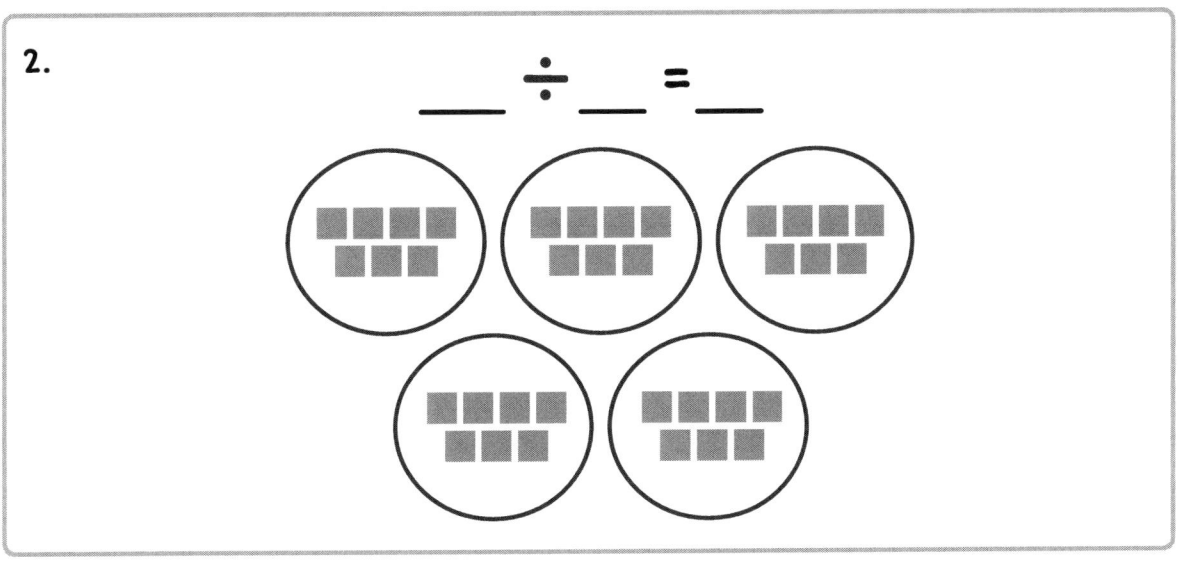

3. ___ ÷ ___ = ___

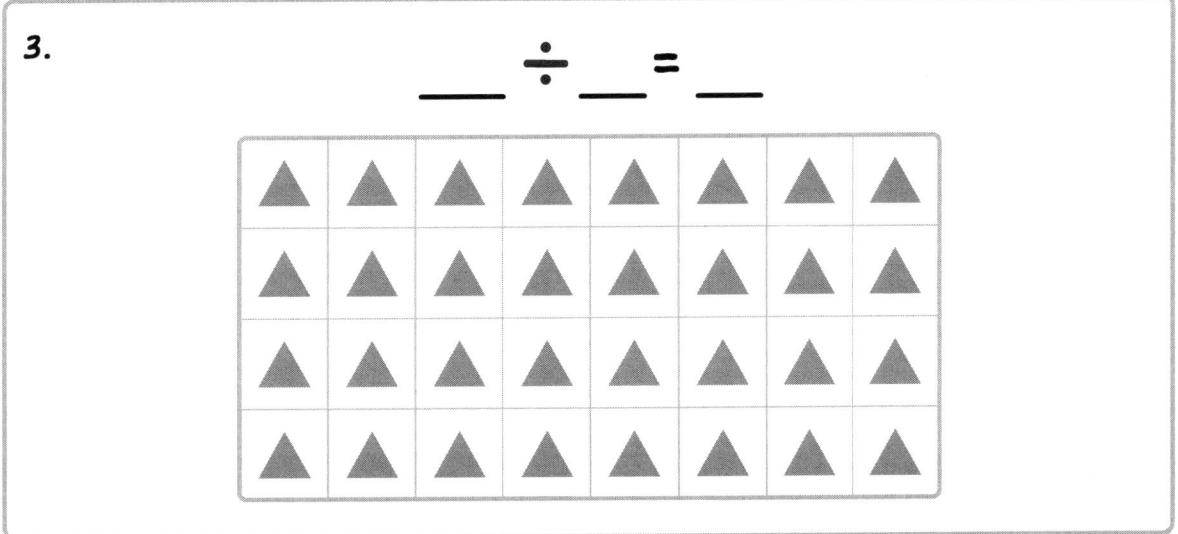

4. ___ ÷ ___ = ___

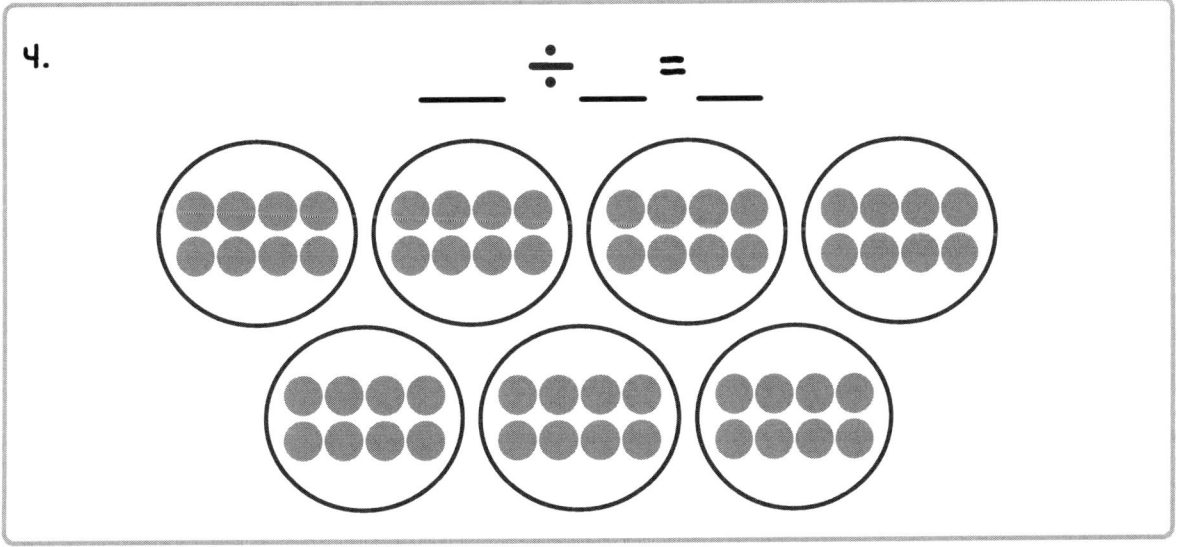

3.5 Applying Division Strategies

5.

___ ÷ ___ = ___

Name: _____ Date: _____

Read and Write to Solve!
Use what you know about multiplication pictures to solve the problems.

Do you remember the parts of a division sentence? Draw a circle around the dividend Draw a square around the divisor. Draw a triangle around the quotient.

$$\underline{15} \div \underline{5} = \underline{3}$$

Read about the astronauts and their missions. Then write the correct dividend, divisor, and quotient on the lines.

Example:

There are 20 astronauts going to the Moon. There are 5 rockets. Each rocket has 4 astronauts on board.

$$\underline{20} \div \underline{5} = \underline{4}$$

1. There are 24 astronauts going to the Moon. There are 8 rockets. Each rocket has 3 astronauts on board.

   ___ ÷ ___ = ___

4.1 Explain Division

34

Next page

2. There are 35 astronauts going to Mars. There are 5 rockets. Each rocket has 7 astronauts on board.

___ ÷ ___ = ___

3. There are 48 astronauts going to the Moon. There are 6 rockets. Each rocket has 8 astronauts on board.

___ ÷ ___ = ___

4. There are 54 astronauts going to Mars. There are 9 rockets. Each rocket has 6 astronauts on board.

___ ÷ ___ = ___

Name: _____ Date: _____

Trace and Divide!
Create division pictures to solve division sentences.

Use your counters to count out the total number in each division sentence. Then, make equal groups of counters in each circle. Trace the counters to create a picture. Then use your picture to solve the division sentence.

Example:

$$21 \div 7 = 3$$

1.

$$36 \div 6 = \_\_$$

4.2 Use Pictures to Divide

2.

$$40 \div 8 = \underline{}$$

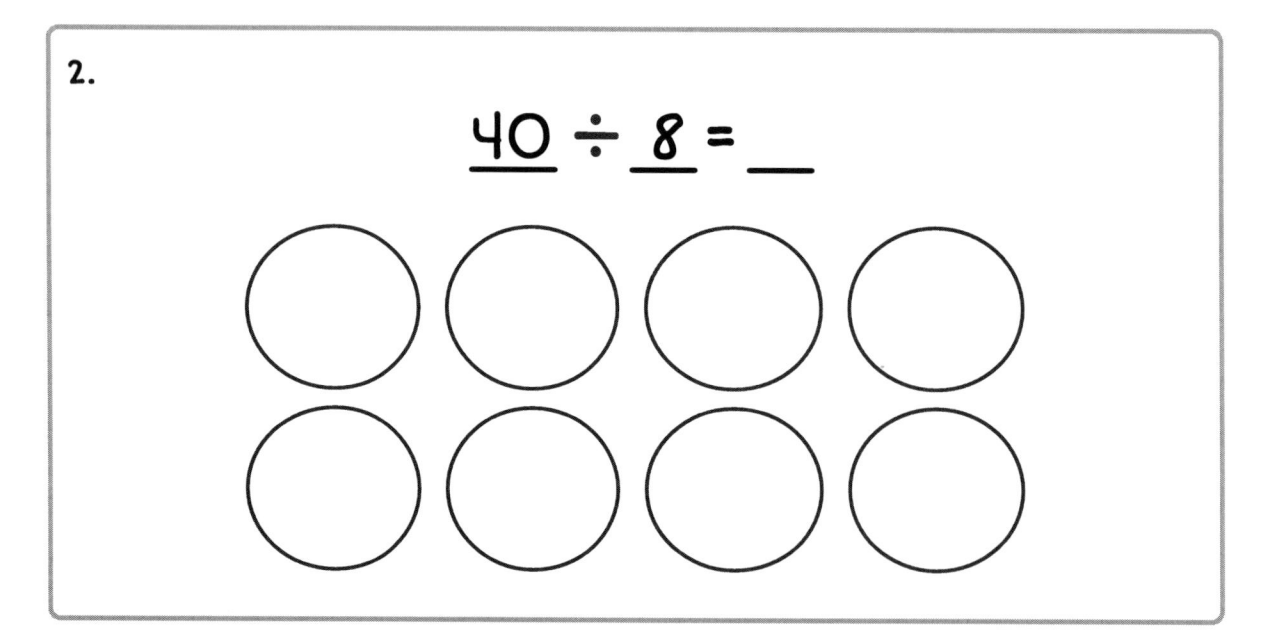

3.

$$56 \div 7 = \underline{}$$

4.2 Use Pictures to Divide

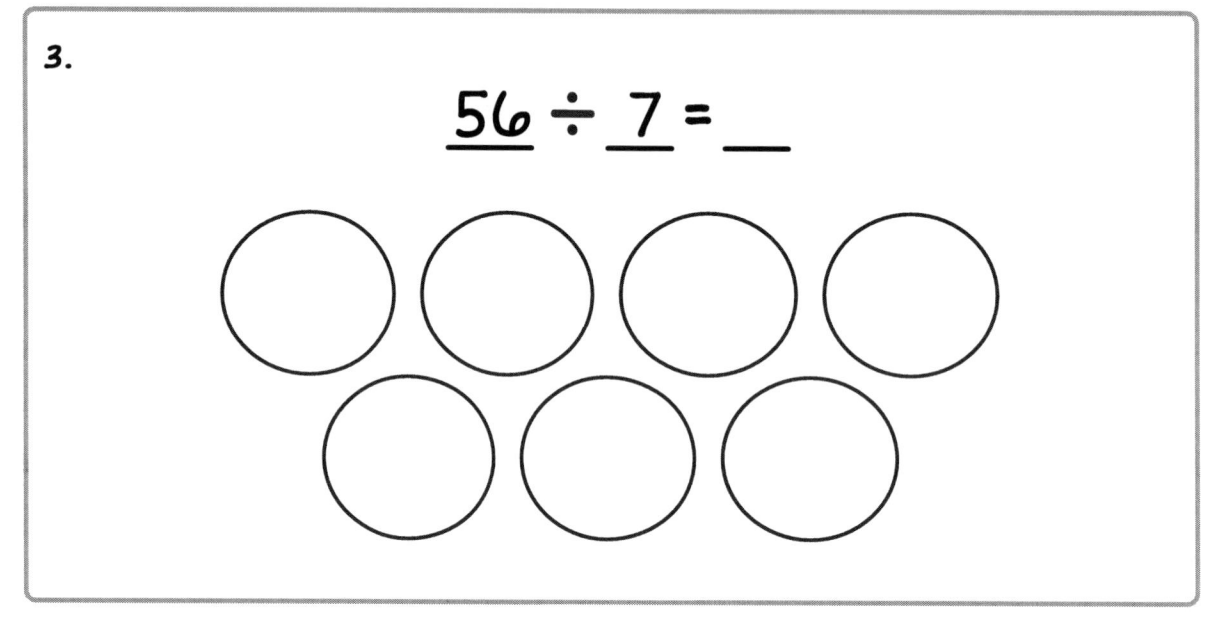

Name: _____ Date: _____

Division with Arrays
Create arrays to solve division sentences.

Get out the correct number of counters. Number the rows you need. Place the counters in the correct numbers of rows and columns. Trace the counters to create an array. Then number the columns. Use your array to solve the division sentence.

Example:

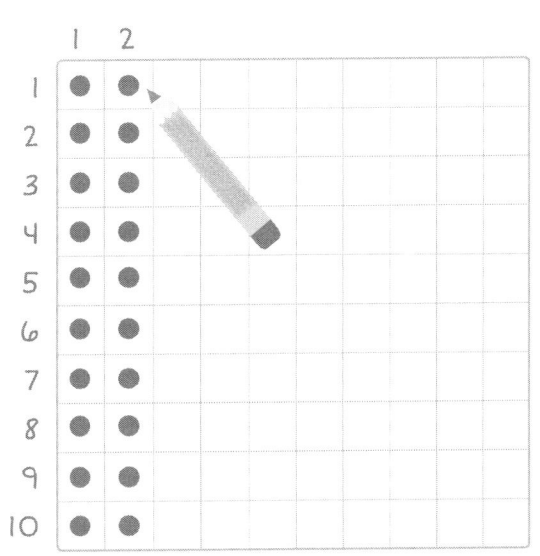

$20 \div 10 = \underline{2}$

1. $28 \div 7 = \underline{}$

4.3 Use Arrays to Divide

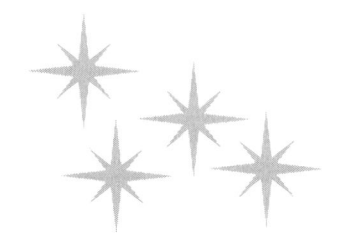

2. 40 ÷ 4 = ___

3. 64 ÷ 8 = ___

39   4.3 Use Arrays to Divide

Name: _____ Date: _____

Write and Divide!
Use an input/output table to solve a division sentence.

Look at the division sentence and the table. Put a circle around the dividend in the table. Put a square around the divisor in the table. Put a triangle around the quotient in the table.

$20 \div 4 = 5$

Input	Output
4	1
8	2
12	3
16	4
20	5
24	6
28	7

Rule: ÷ 4

Fill out the missing quotients in the output column of each table. Then use the table to find the quotient of the division sentence.

Example:

$12 \div 2 = \boxed{6}$

Input	Output
2	1
4	_2_
6	_3_
8	4
10	5
12	_6_
14	7

Rule: ÷ 2

4.4 Dividing with Input/Output Tables

1.

$30 \div 5 = \square$

Input	Output
5	1
10	2
15	3
20	4
25	___
30	___
35	___

Rule: ÷5

2.

$32 \div 8 = \square$

Input	Output
8	___
16	2
24	3
32	___
40	___
48	6
56	7

Rule: ÷8

3.

$42 \div 6 = \square$

Input	Output
6	1
12	___
18	___
24	4
30	5
36	6
42	___

Rule: ÷6

4.4 Dividing with Input/Output Tables

Create and Prove!

Use what you know about division strategies to check a quotient.

Complete the division strategy shown. Then use it to check the quotient. Write the correct quotient on the line.

Example:

$$25 \div 5 = 5$$

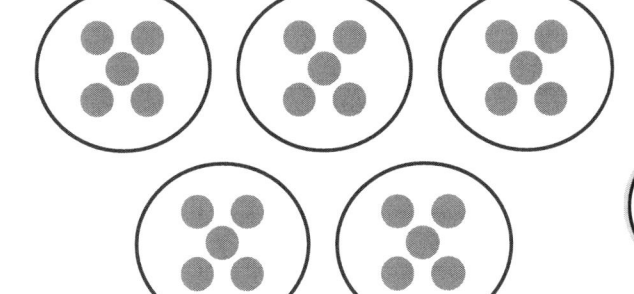

Write the same quotient from the division sentence if it is correct

The correct quotient is 5.

1.

$$40 \div 8 = 6$$

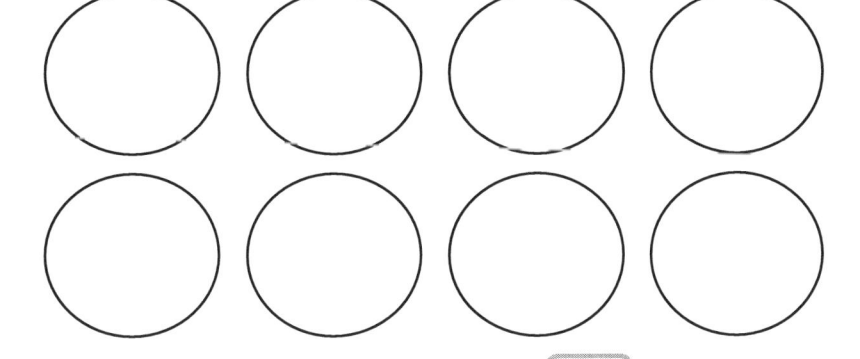

The correct quotient is ☐.

4.5 Problem Solve: Reasoning with Division Facts

2.

$$64 \div 8 = 8$$

___ - __ - __ - __ - __ - __ - __ - __ - __ = 0

The correct quotient is ☐.

3.

$$70 \div 7 = 9$$

The correct quotient is ☐.

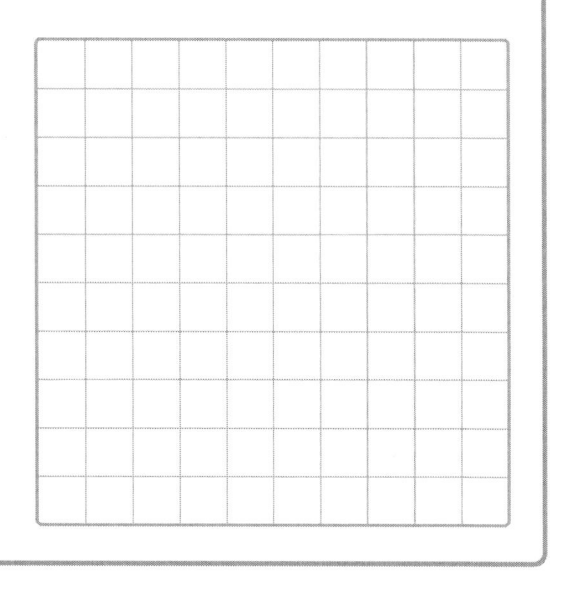

4. **Think About it!** Which division strategy do you like the best? Draw a picture of it in the box. Then write one sentence about why you like using the strategy.

Name: _____ Date: _____

Round and Color!

Use what you know about rounding to round whole numbers to the nearest 10 or 100.

Round each number to the nearest 10 or 100. Draw a line under the place you are rounding to. Write the multiples of 10 or 100 that your number is between in each box underneath the number. Then write the nearest 10 or 100 in the box.

Next, look for the answer you found on parts of the flamingo. Color the flamingo the color next to the problem you solved!

Example: Round to the nearest 10.

1<u>3</u>6 |140|

|130| |140| Brown

Color the part on the flamingo brown that has a 140 on it.

1. Round to the nearest 10.

93   [   ]

[   ] [   ]   Pink

5.2 Round Whole Numbers

44

2. Round to the nearest 100.

298

Orange

3. Round to the nearest 10.

365

Red

4. Round to the nearest 100.

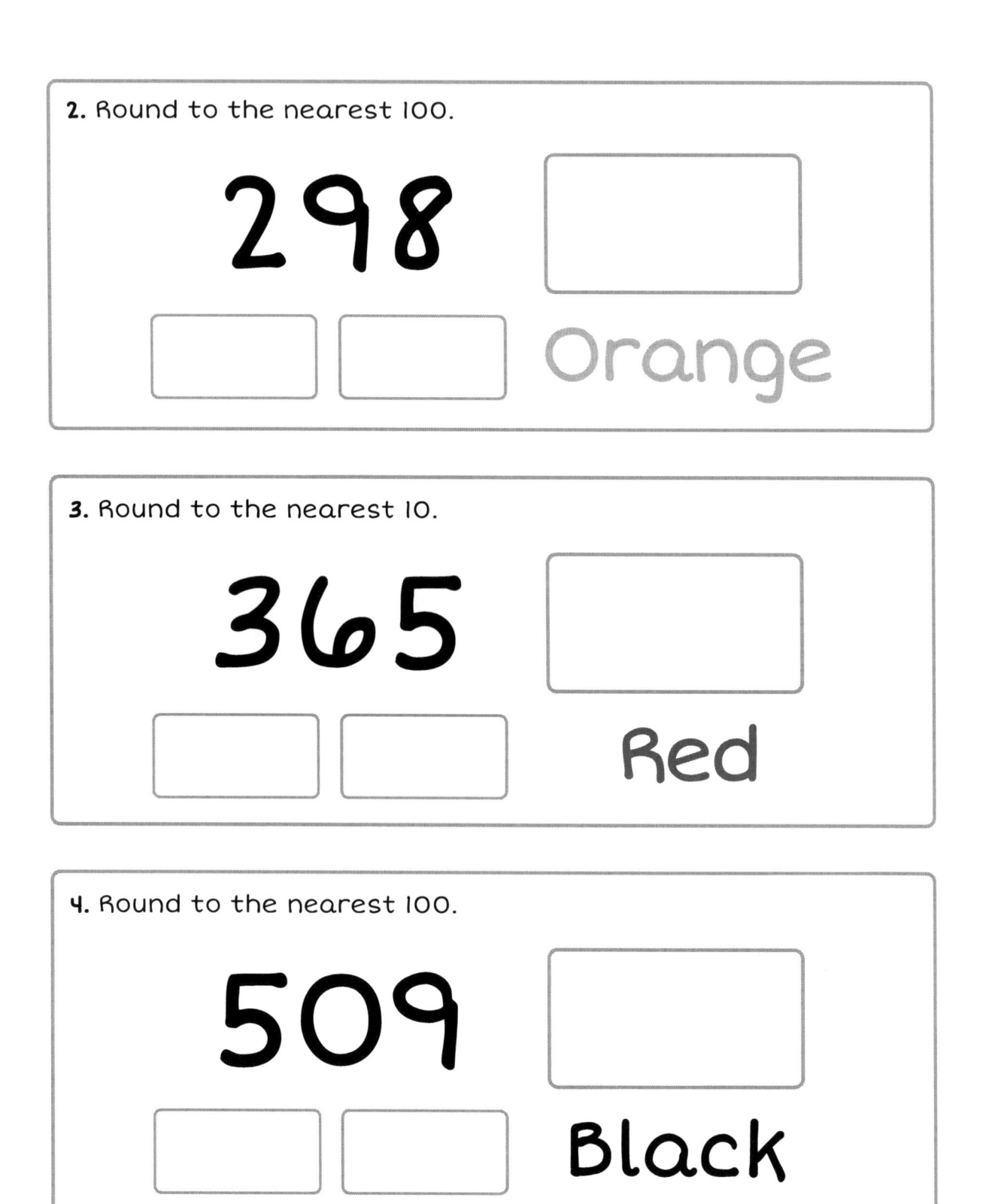

509

Black

45

5.2 Round Whole Numbers

Next page

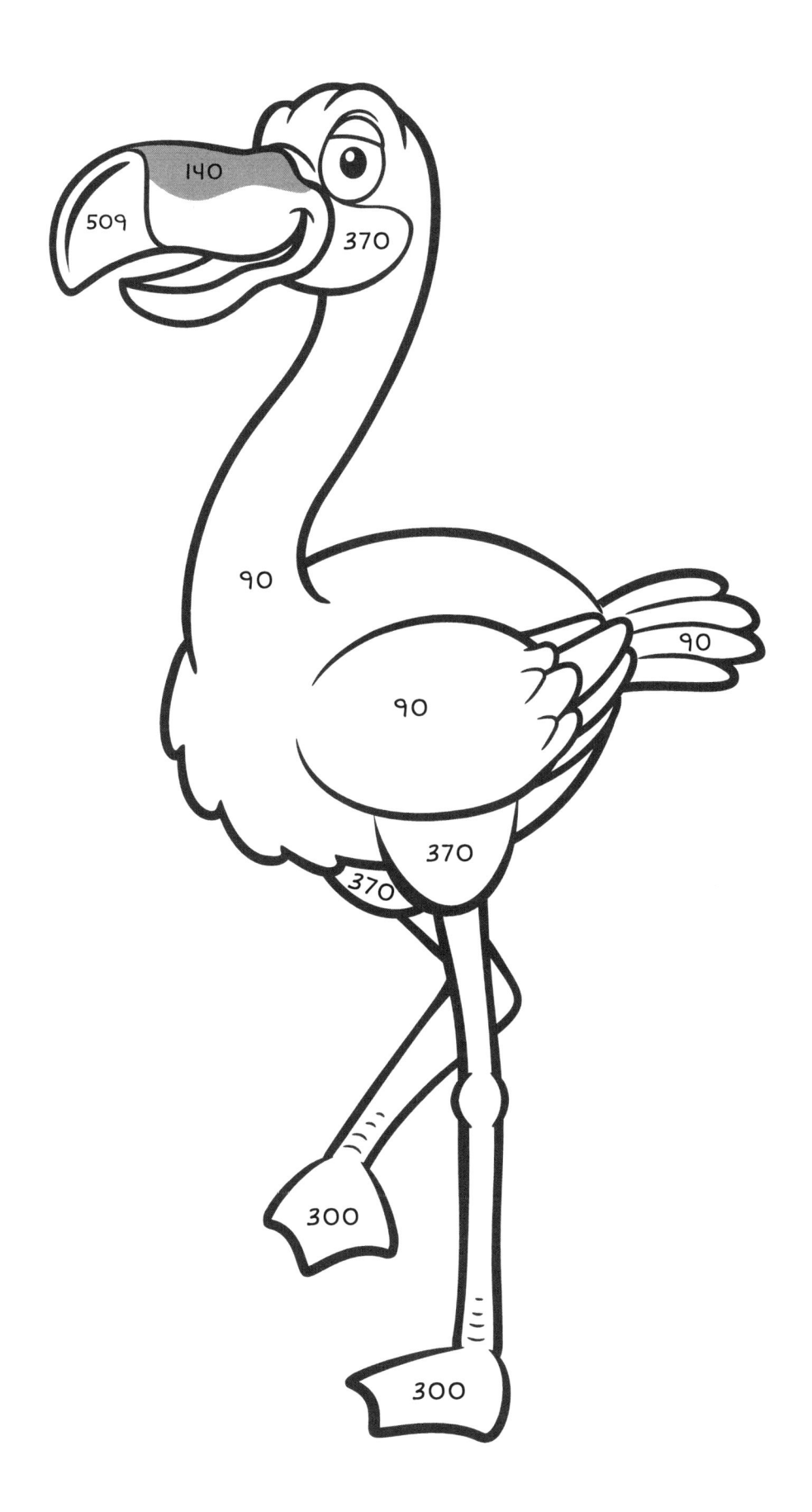

5.2 Round Whole Numbers

46

Name: _____ Date: _____

Solve and Spell!

Draw place-value blocks and use ungrouping to find the sum of addition problems.

Can you draw place-value blocks or use ungrouping to solve addition problems? Find the sum of each problem by drawing place-value blocks or ungrouping. Draw a ☐ for the flats, a | for the rods, and a ☐ for the unit cubes. Then, use your answers to write the letters on the lines to see the name of a savanna bird!

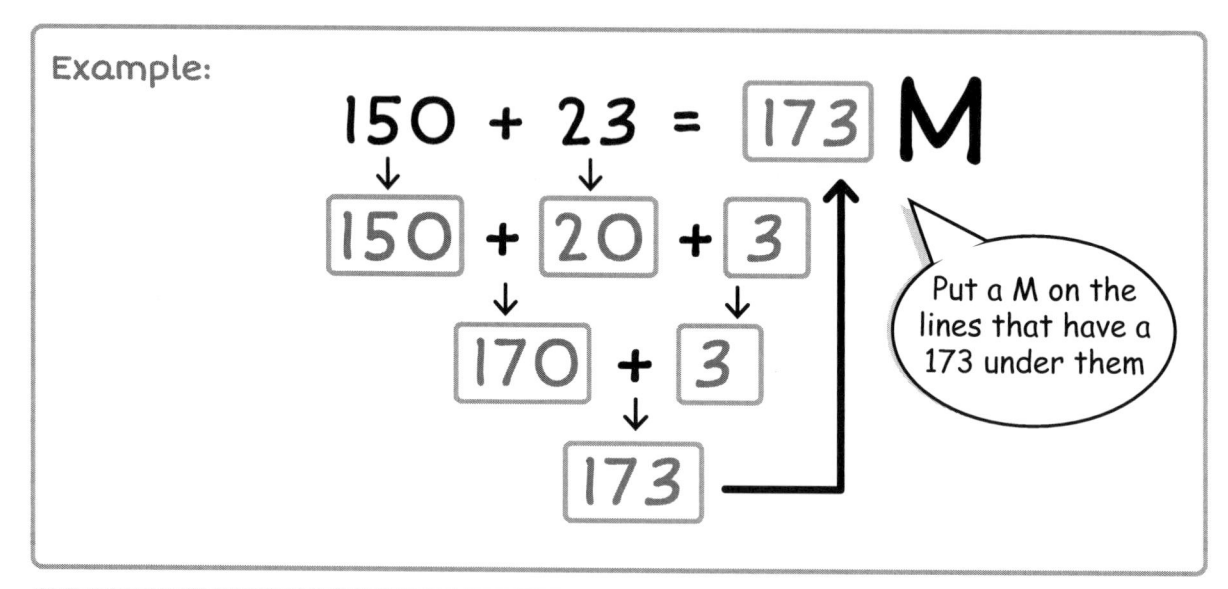

Example:

150 + 23 = 173 **M**

150 + 20 + 3

170 + 3

173

Put a M on the lines that have a 173 under them

Example: 150 + 23 = 173 **M**

Hundreds	Tens	Ones
☐	||||| ||	☐ ☐ ☐
1	7	3

Put a M on the lines that have a 173 under them

47

5.3 Add Whole Numbers

Next page

1. Draw place-value blocks to find the sum.

327 + 50 = ☐   A

Hundreds	Tens	Ones

2. Use ungrouping to find the sum.

500 + 208 = ☐   K

5.3 Add Whole Numbers

3. Draw place-value blocks to find the sum.

321 + 513 = ☐   O

Hundreds	Tens	Ones

2. Use ungrouping to find the sum.

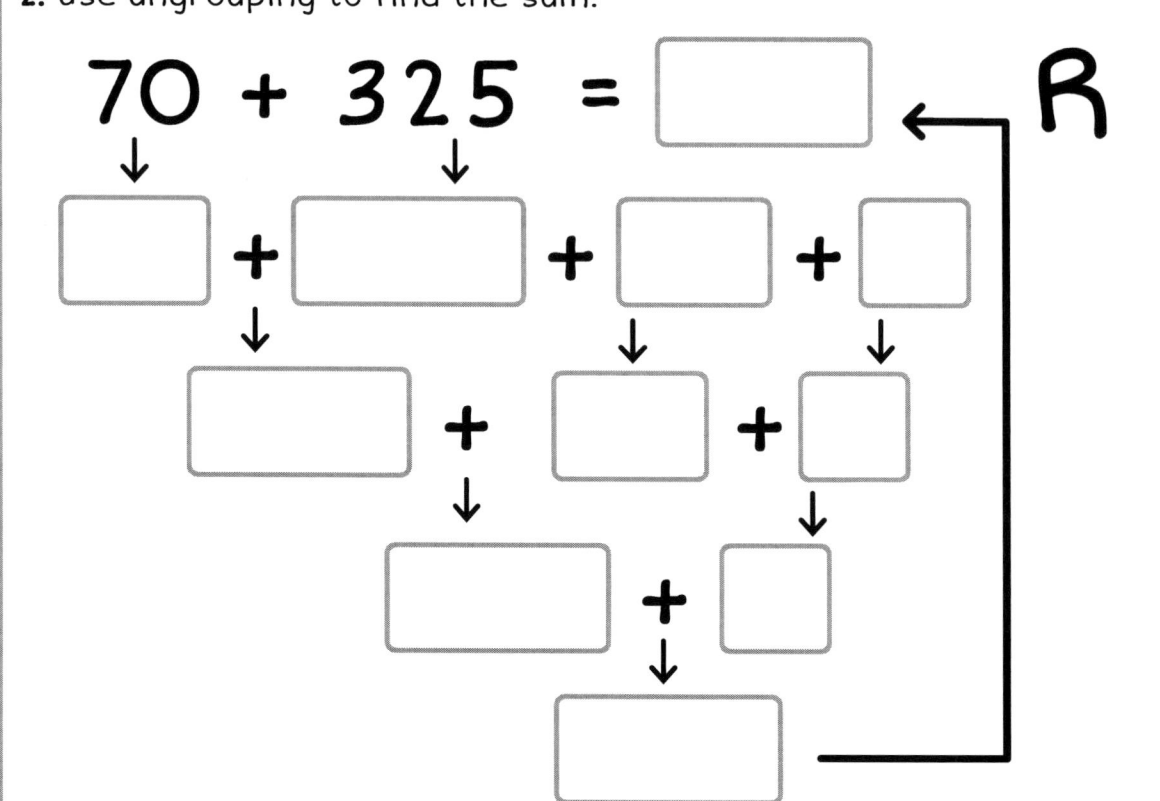

70 + 325 = ☐   R

☐ + ☐ + ☐ + ☐

☐ + ☐ + ☐

☐ + ☐

☐

49

5.3 Add Whole Numbers

Next page

M ___ ___ ___ B _ U ST ___ ___ ___
173 377 395 377   834   834 395 708

5.3 Add Whole Numbers

50

Name: _____ Date: _____

Solve and Connect!

Use the place-value chart or ungrouping to find the difference of each subtraction problem.

Can you use a place-value chart and ungrouping to solve subtraction problems? Find the difference of each problem by drawing place-value blocks in the charts or ungrouping. Use your answers to connect the correct dots and help Ava complete her trip!

Show the minuend and take away the blocks that show the subtrahend!

Example:

$$534 - 224 = 310$$

Hundreds	Tens	Ones
☐ ☐ ☐ ✕ ✕	⎮ ✕ ✕	✕ ✕ ✕ ✕
3	1	0

Example:

534 − 224 = 310

534 − 200 − 20 − 4

334 − 20 − 4

314 − 4

310

51

5.4 Subtract Whole Numbers

Next page

1. Use ungrouping to find the difference.

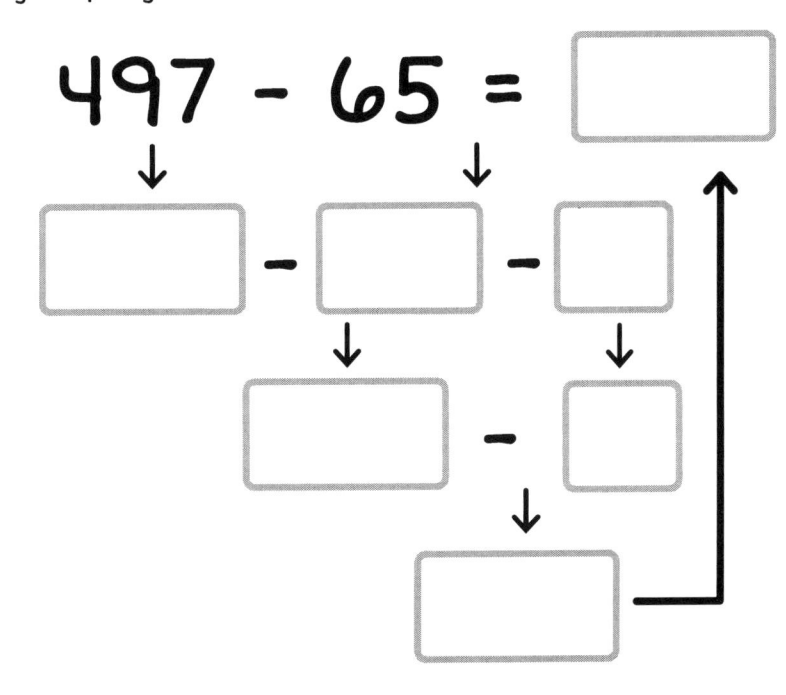

$$497 - 65 = \boxed{}$$

```
   ↓           ↓
[    ] - [    ] - [    ]
            ↓        ↓
         [    ] - [    ]
                    ↓
                 [    ]
```

2. Use place-value blocks to find the difference.

$$579 - 65 = \boxed{}\boxed{}\boxed{}$$

Hundreds	Tens	Ones

5.4 Subtract Whole Numbers

3. Use ungrouping to find the difference.

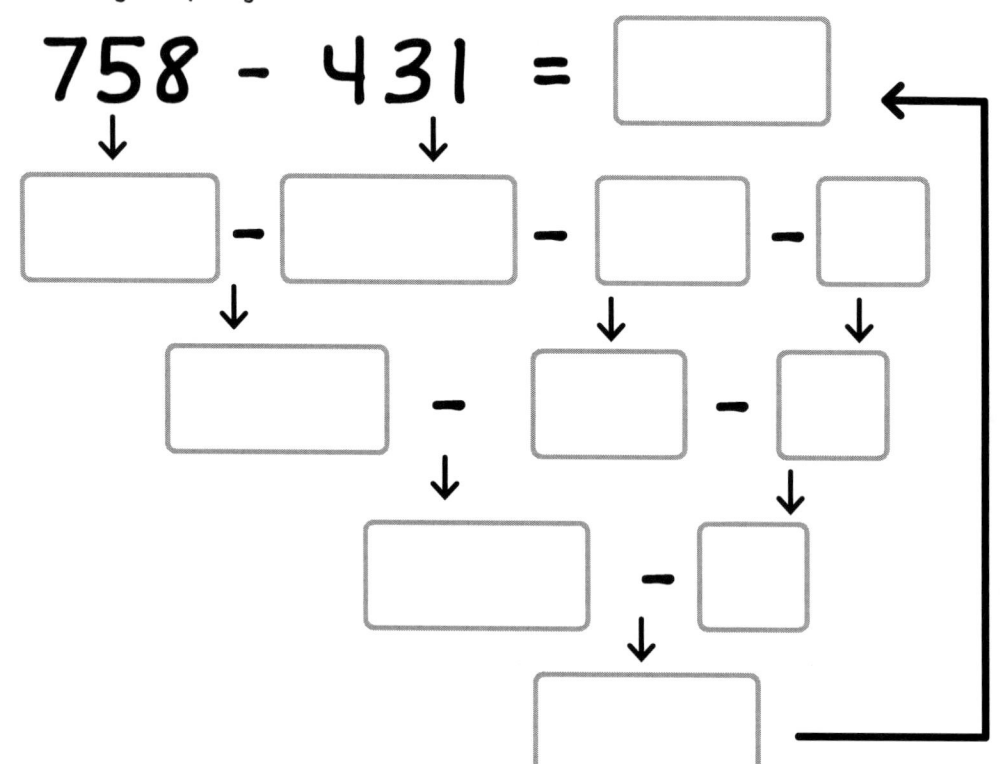

758 - 431 = ☐

☐ - ☐ - ☐ - ☐

☐ - ☐ - ☐

☐ - ☐

☐

4. Draw place-value blocks to find the difference.

899 - 311 = ☐☐☐

Hundreds	Tens	Ones

53

5.4 Subtract Whole Numbers

Next page

Connect the dots that match your answers in order. The correct answers will take Ava to see each group of animals and then to the end of her trip!

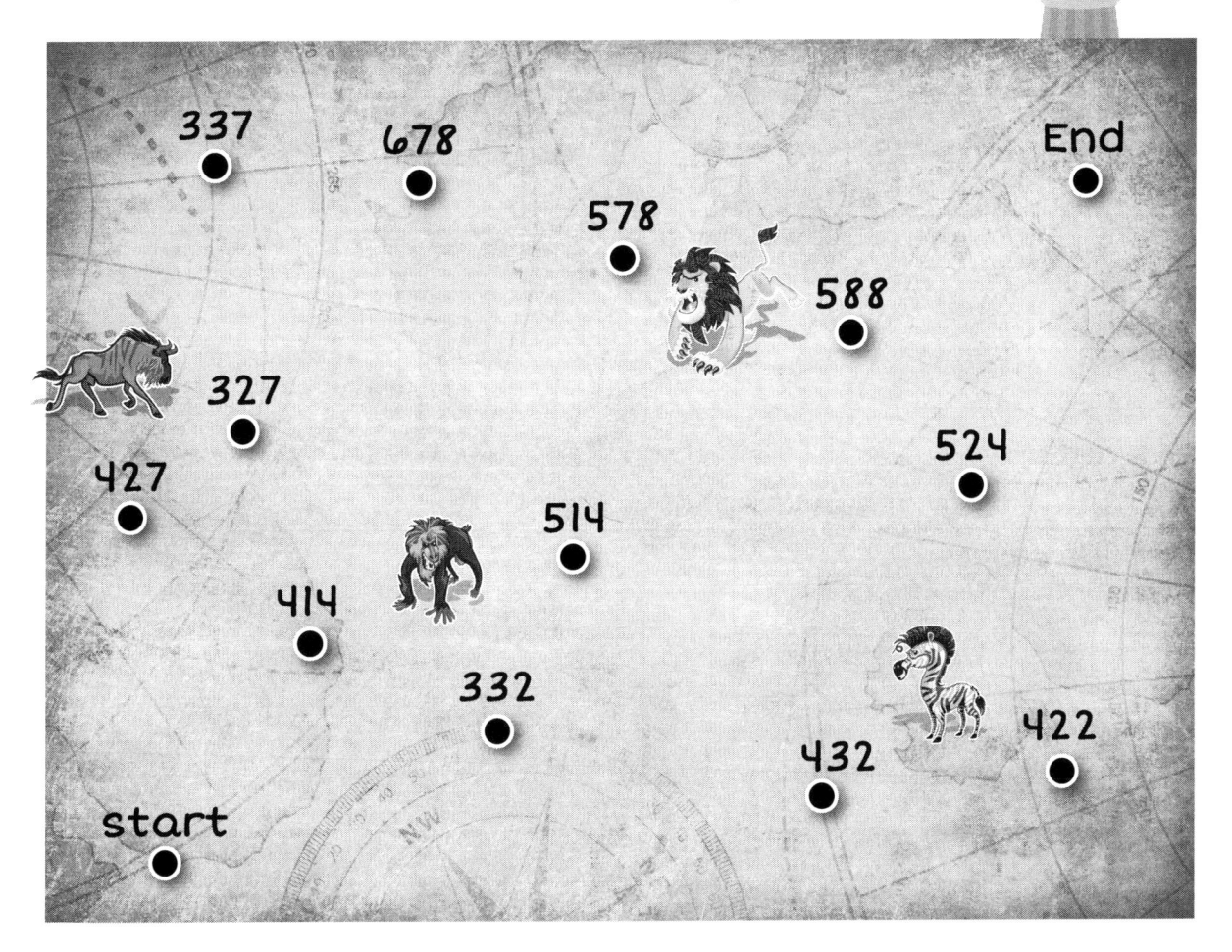

337 678   End
         578
              588
327
        514
427
   414
      332
                432 422

start

5.4 Subtract Whole Numbers

Name: _____   Date: _____

Safari Supply Multiplication

Use what you have learned about multiplying multiples of 10 and a 1-digit number.

Can you help Logan count the supplies collected for the school safari? Each problem has a box with a supply in it. Solve each multiplication sentence, and write the product on each line. Write the correct product next to each supply on the supply list. Then cut out your list to decorate and turn in!

Example:
Do not forget to cross out the 0 and put it at the end of the product!
Find the canteen on the list and write the correct product next to the picture.

6̶0̶ x 4 = __240__

1. 10 x 9 = _____

2. 80 x 2 = _____

55

5.5 Multiply Whole Numbers

Next page

3. 30 x 6 = _____

4. 50 x 8 = _____

5. 90 x 5 = _____

6. 40 x 7 = _____

5.5 Multiply Whole Numbers

240

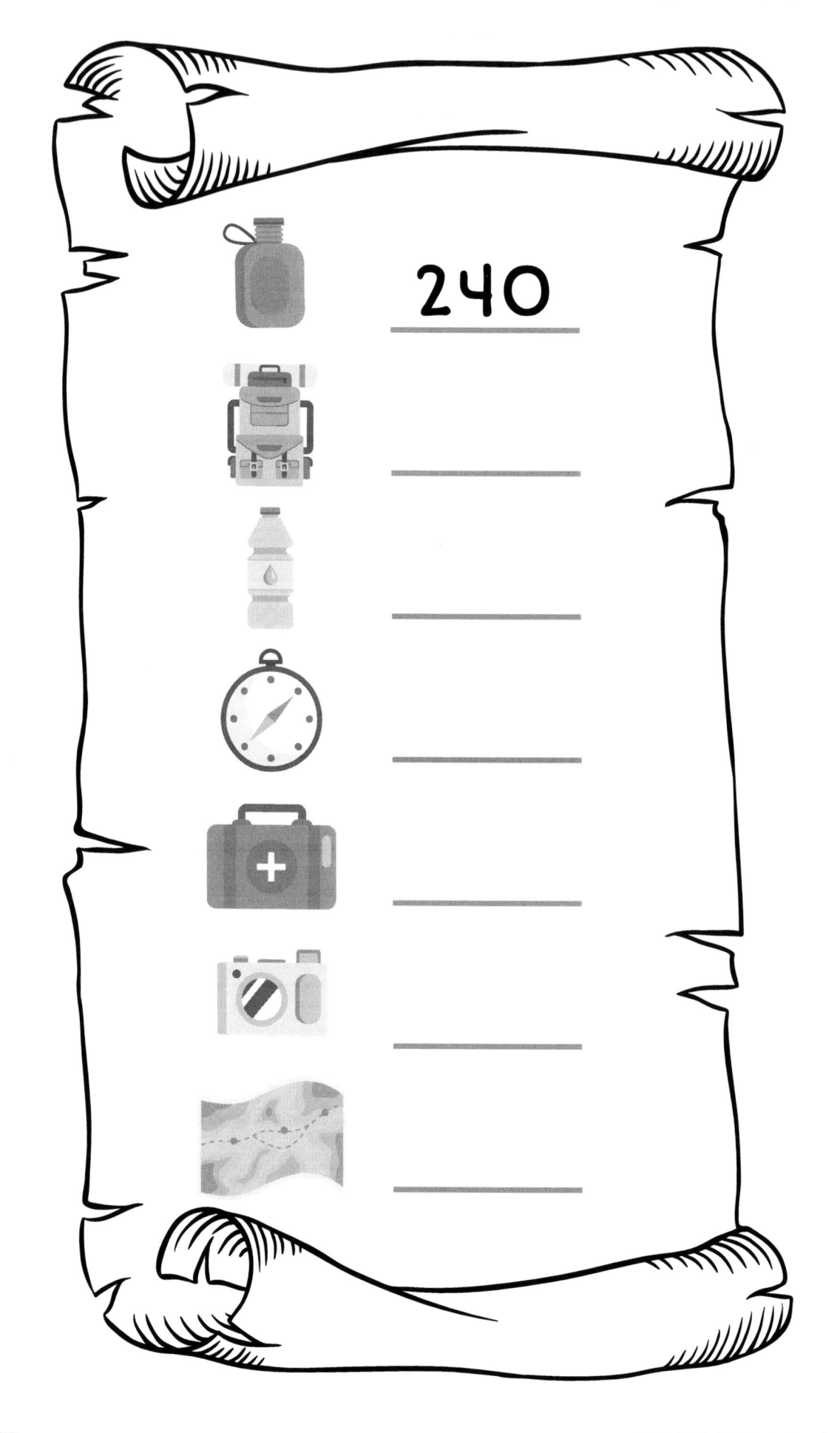

Zoe's Leaf Collection

Find the sum of each vertical and horizontal addition sentence. Find the sum in the key. Color the leaf the color of the matching sum to see Zoe's leaf collection!.

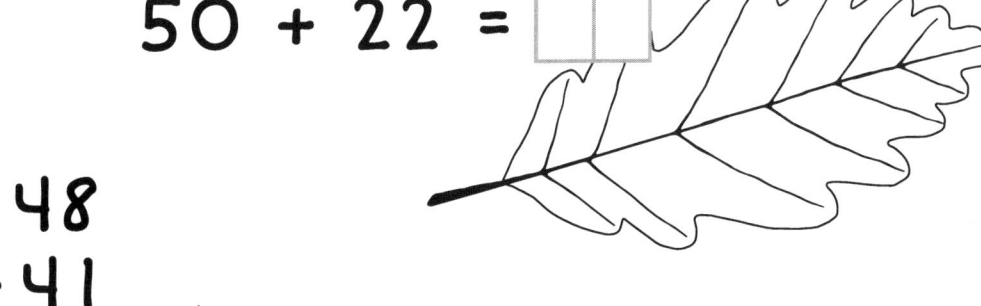

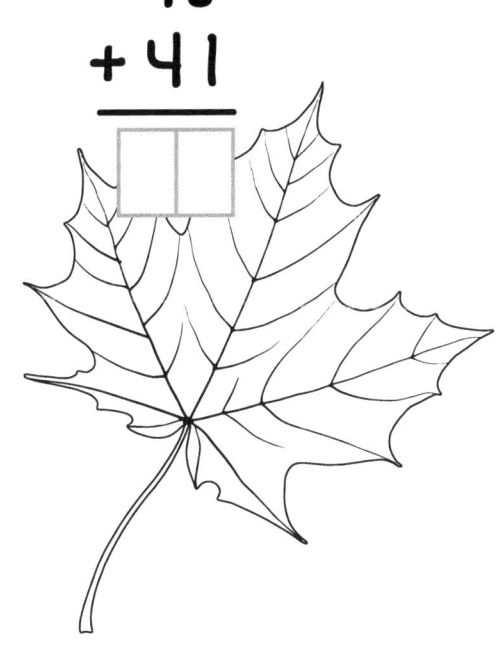

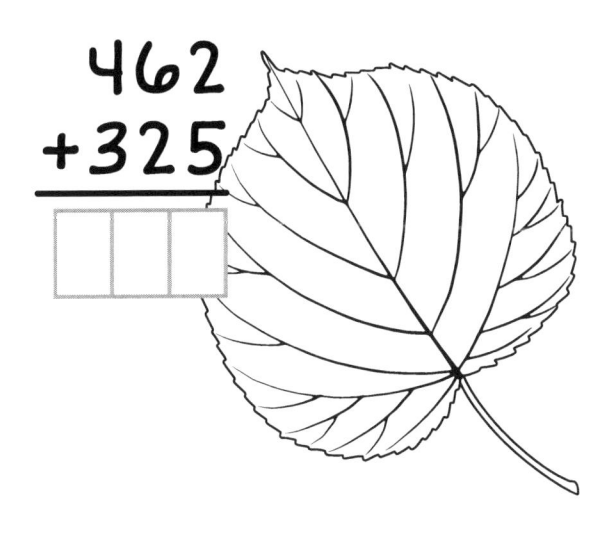

My Fall Leaf Collection

50 + 22 = ☐☐

48
+41
———
☐☐

462
+325
———
☐☐☐

6.1 Add Without Carrying

203 + 102 = ☐☐☐

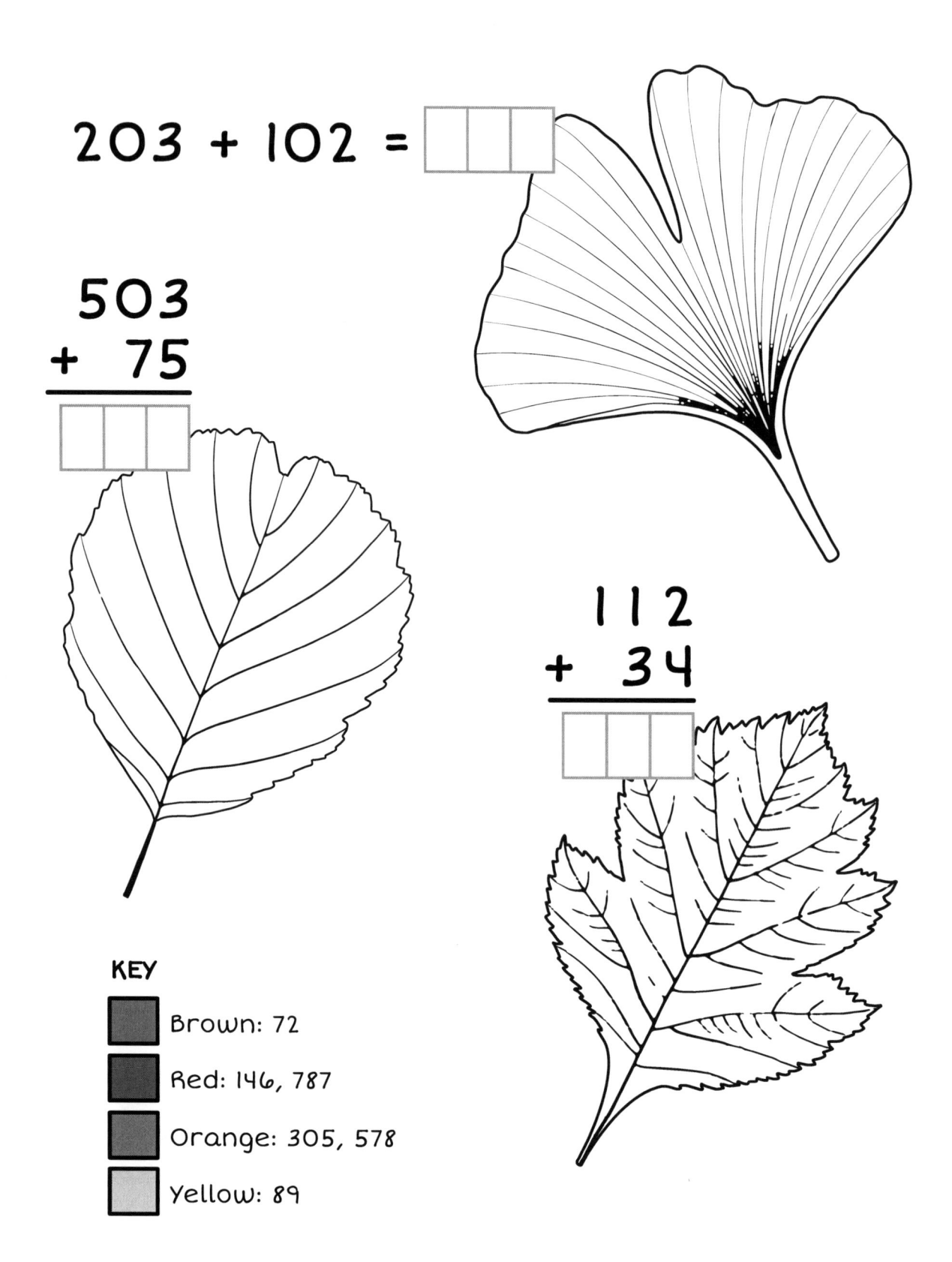

503
+ 75
―――
☐☐☐

112
+ 34
―――
☐☐☐

KEY

Brown: 72

Red: 146, 787

Orange: 305, 578

Yellow: 89

6.1 Add Without Carrying

Name: _____ Date: _____

Add and Color!

Use what you know about regrouping to find the sums of 2-digit and 3-digit numbers.

Find the sum of each addition sentence. Do not forget to carry to regroup if you need to! Look for the sums on the picture. Color each space the correct matching color.

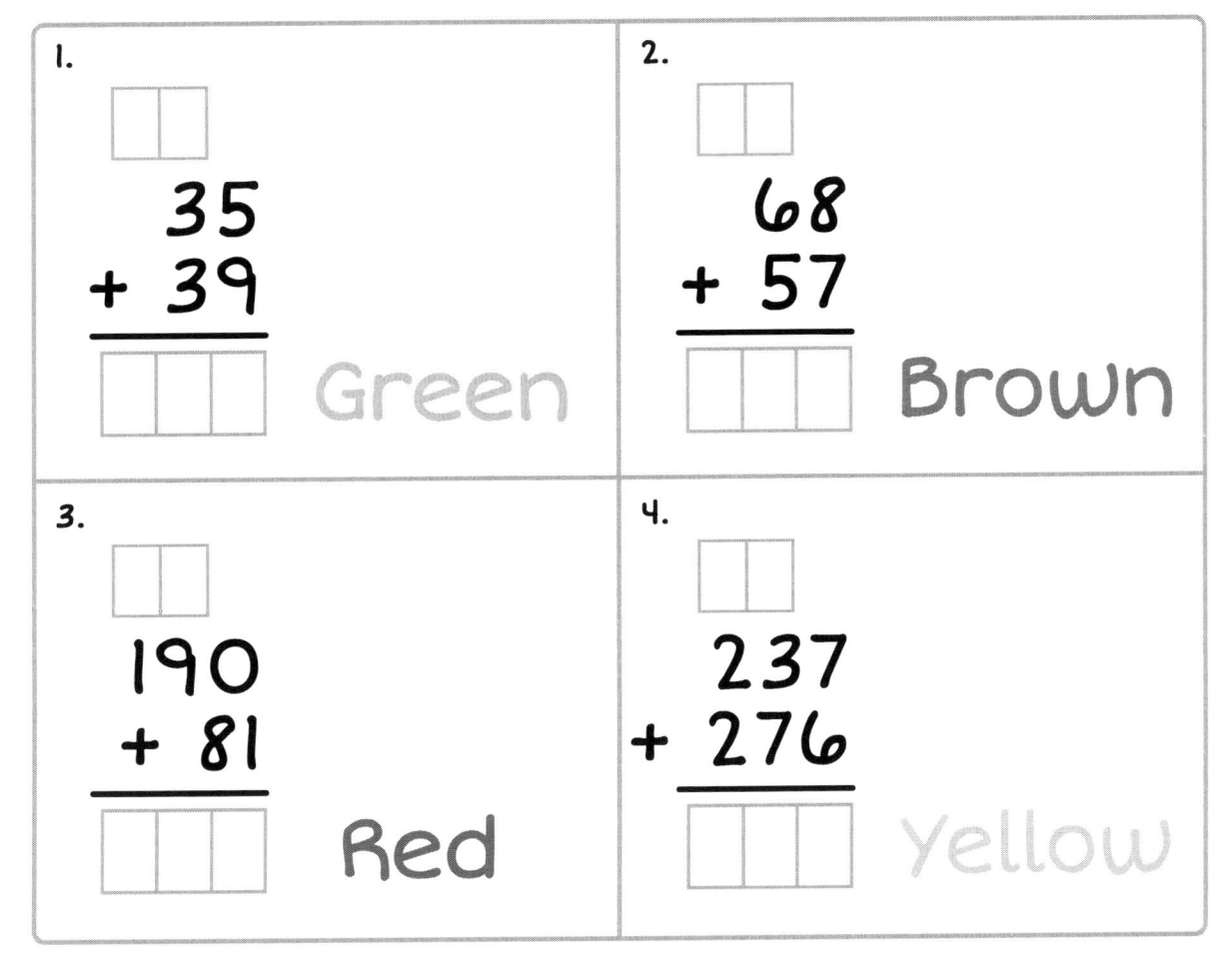

Example:

Only regroup when you need to!

```
  1
 562
+241
─────
 803
```
Purple

Find the parts of the picture with 803. Color them purple

1.
```
  35
+ 39
─────
```
Green

2.
```
  68
+ 57
─────
```
Brown

3.
```
 190
+ 81
─────
```
Red

4.
```
 237
+276
─────
```
Yellow

6.2 Add with Carrying to Regroup

60
Next page

6.2 Add with Carrying to Regroup

Name: _____ Date: _____

Scarecrow Subtraction

Solve vertical and horizontal subtraction sentences with 2-digit and 3-digit numbers.

Find the difference of each vertical and horizontal subtraction sentence. Write each digit of the differences in the correct boxes. Then use your answers to write the letters on the lines to see the answer to the joke on the second page!

Example:

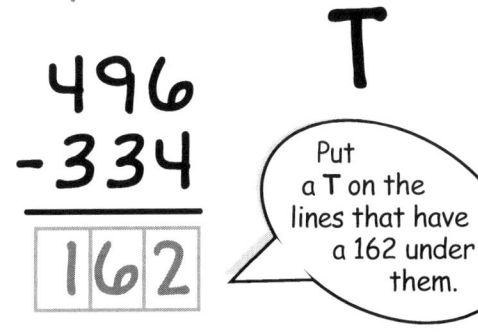

$$\begin{array}{r} 496 \\ -334 \\ \hline 162 \end{array}$$ T

Put a T on the lines that have a 162 under them.

1.
$$\begin{array}{r} 49 \\ -21 \\ \hline \end{array}$$ U

2.
$$\begin{array}{r} 98 \\ -53 \\ \hline \end{array}$$ S

3.
$$\begin{array}{r} 364 \\ -34 \\ \hline \end{array}$$ D

4.
$$\begin{array}{r} 277 \\ -206 \\ \hline \end{array}$$ F

6.3 Subtract Without Regrouping

Why didn't the scarecrow eat his dinner?

Because he was $\underset{45}{\_}\underset{162}{T}\underset{28}{\_}\underset{71}{\_}\underset{71}{\_}\underset{330}{E}\underset{}{\_}$!

Name: _____ Date: _____

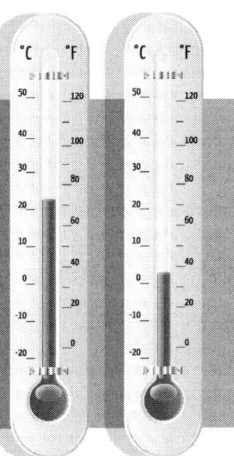

Subtract and Match!

Use what you know about regrouping while subtracting to solve problems.

Can you help Caleb bake pies with his family? Solve each subtraction sentence and write the digits of the difference in each box. Each problem has pie next to it. Write the correct difference on the oven with the matching pie to set the correct temperature.

Example:

[2][17]
3̷7̷1
− 1 9 0
―――
[1][8][1]

Cross out the digits of the minuend on your own. Only regroup when you need to!

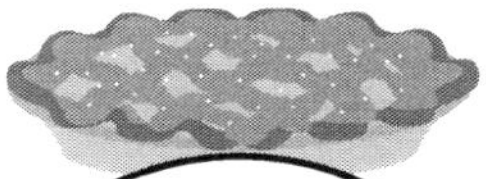

Find the oven with this pie in it. Then write the temperature in the box of the oven.

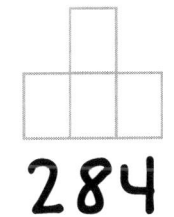

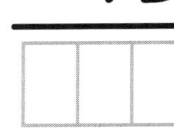

1.
   82
 − 59
 ―――

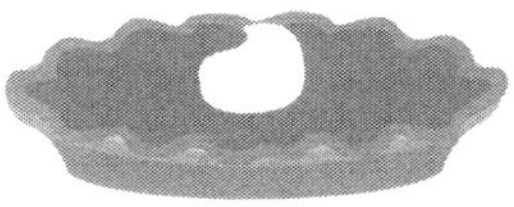

2.
   90
 − 46
 ―――

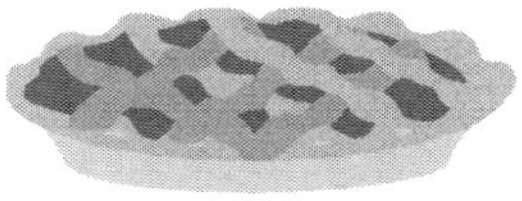

3.
   284
 − 73
 ―――

6.4 Subtract with Borrowing to Regroup

64

Next page

4.
```
  231
-  88
```

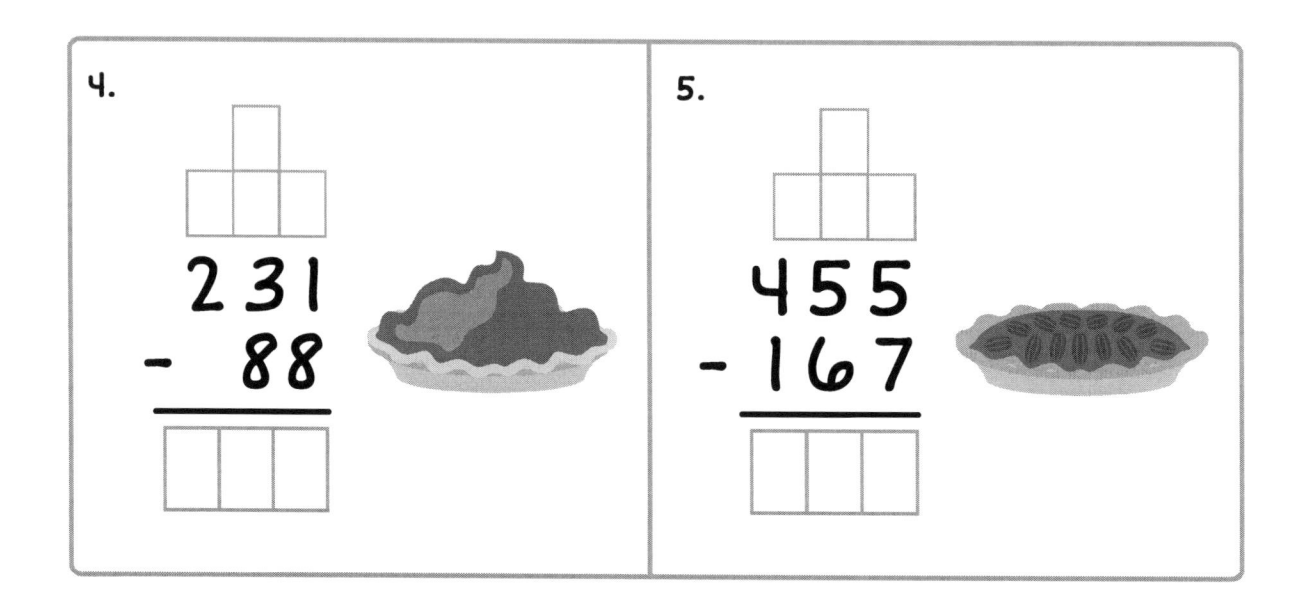

5.
```
  455
- 167
```

181

6.4 Subtract with Borrowing to Regroup

Name: _____ Date: _____

Find and Solve!
Read and solve word problems with addition or subtraction.

Madelyn needs help putting away the corn from the harvest! Read each word problem and look for the key words in the circles. Then, decide if you need to add or subtract. Write the correct sign in the box. Then, solve the addition or subtraction problem. Do not forget to carry over or borrow when you need to!

Example:

Madelyn has 76 ears of corn to put away. She puts away 28 ears of corn. How many ears of corn (remain)?

$$\begin{array}{r} 6\,16 \\ \cancel{7}\cancel{6} \\ -\ 28 \\ \hline 48 \end{array}$$ ears of corn

Only fill the boxes you need! Only regroup when you need to!

1.

Madelyn has 57 ears of corn to put away. Then she gets 63 (more) ears of corn. How many ears of corn does she need to put away (in all)?

$$\begin{array}{r} 63 \\ \square\ 57 \\ \hline \end{array}$$ ears of corn

6.5 Problem Solving: Add and Subtract

2.

Madelyn has 193 ears of corn to put away. She puts away 81 ears of corn. How many ears of corn are (left) for Madelyn to put away?

☐ 193
  　81
  ___

ears of corn

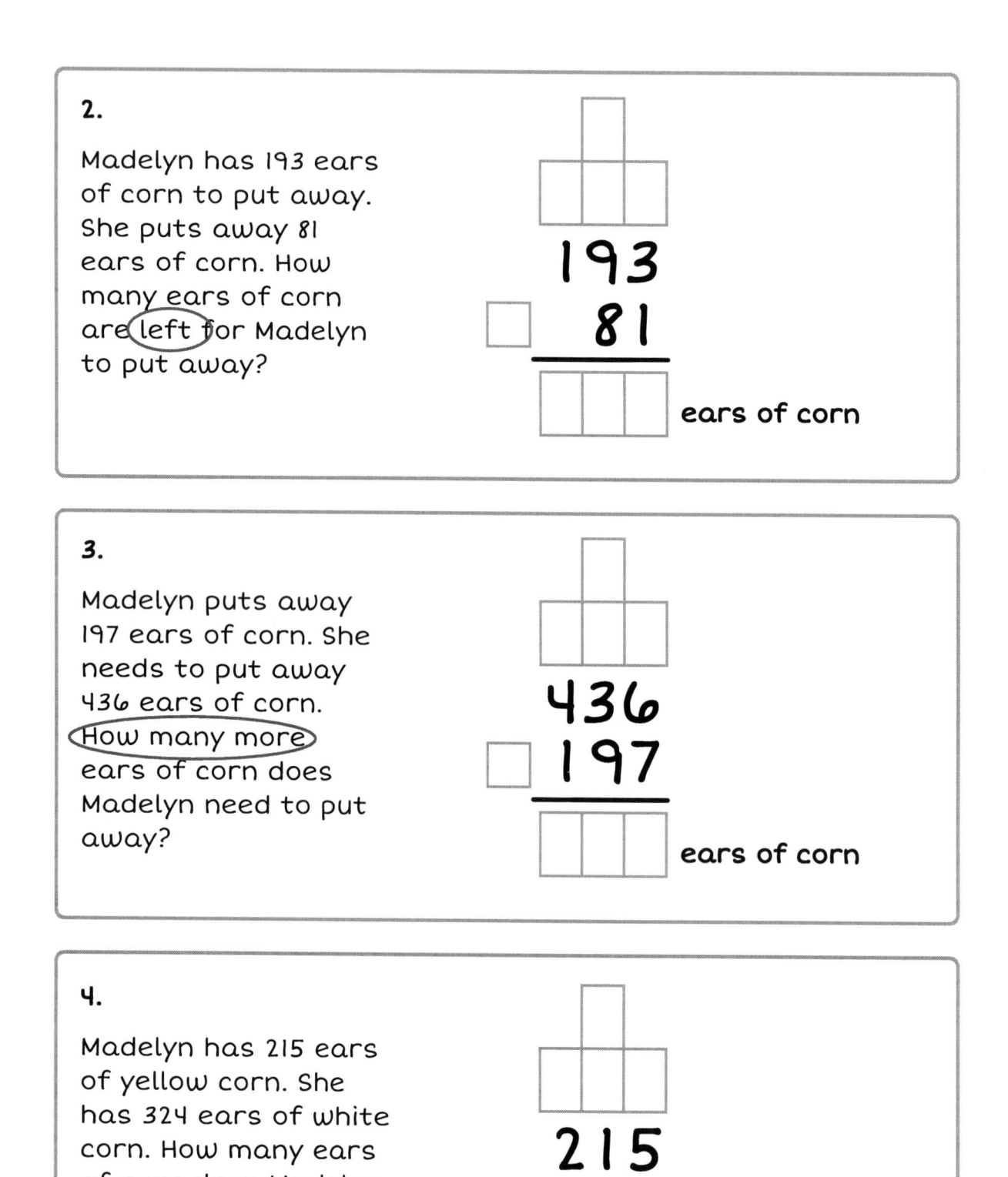

3.

Madelyn puts away 197 ears of corn. She needs to put away 436 ears of corn. (How many more) ears of corn does Madelyn need to put away?

☐ 436
  197
  ___

ears of corn

4.

Madelyn has 215 ears of yellow corn. She has 324 ears of white corn. How many ears of corn does Madelyn have (altogether)?

☐ 215
  324
  ___

ears of corn

Challenge: Can you write and solve your own word problem? Decide if you want to add or subtract. Circle the words you want to use. Then, write the correct key words on the lines. To solve your problem, write the correct sign in the box and add or subtract!

Madelyn and her aunt have 315 ears of corn.

They will _____ 176 ears of corn. How

many ears of corn are _____?

```
      ☐
     315
  ☐  176
  ─────
  ☐☐☐   ears of corn
```

put away

get an extra

there in all

left over

6.5 Problem Solving: Add and Subtract

Name: _____   Date: _____

Read, Write, Solve!
Find the unknown quantity of an equation to solve a word problem.

Zoe needs your help setting her practicing goals for the week! Read each word problem. Then fill out and solve the equations using the word problems and pictures. Write your answers on the lines. Fill out Zoe's schedule with all of your answers when you are done!

Example:
Zoe wants to set a goal for Monday. She wants to play for 30 minutes and then for 40 more minutes. Zoe takes away 15 minutes. How many minutes is her goal for Monday?

Draw your picture here:

$$30 + 40 = 70$$

$$70 - 15 = 55$$

Use any shape for your pictures. Remember an 'X' means you took a shape away.

Monday's goal is to play __55__ minutes.

7.2 Two-Step Word Problems: Addition and Subtraction

Next page

1. Zoe wants to set a goal for Monday. She wants to play for 60 minutes, but then thinks she should play 10 minutes less. Zoe then thinks she should play 20 more minutes. How many minutes is Zoe's goal for Monday?

Draw your picture here:

☐ - ☐ = ☐

☐ + ☐ = ☐

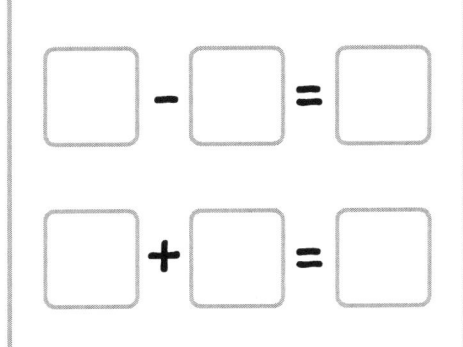

Monday's goal is to play _____ minutes.

2. Zoe wants to set a goal for Tuesday. She wants to play for 25 minutes and then 35 more minutes. Zoe wants to spend 15 of those minutes reading. How many minutes is Zoe's goal for Tuesday?

Draw your picture here:

☐ + ☐ = ☐

☐ - ☐ = ☐

Tuesday's goal is to play _____ minutes.

7.2 Two-Step Word Problems: Addition and Subtraction

3. Zoe wants to set a goal for Wednesday. She wants to play for 56 minutes. She decides to take away 12 minutes to run outside. Then Zoe wants to play for 22 minutes. How many minutes is Zoe's goal for Wednesday?

Draw your picture here:

☐ - ☐ = ☐

☐ + ☐ = ☐

Wednesday's goal is to play _____ minutes.

4. Zoe wants to set a goal for Thursday. She wants to play for 34 minutes. Then she wants to play for 16 more minutes. Zoe decides her goal should be 23 minutes less. How many minutes is Zoe's goal for Thursday?

Draw your picture here:

☐ + ☐ = ☐

☐ - ☐ = ☐

Thursday's goal is to play _____ minutes.

5. Zoe wants to set a goal for Friday. She wants to play for 17 minutes and then 65 minutes. Zoe takes away 39 minutes from her goal. How many minutes is Zoe's goal for Friday?

Draw your picture here:

☐ + ☐ = ☐

☐ - ☐ = ☐

Friday's goal is to play _____ minutes.

Zoe's Practice Goals

Monday	Tuesday	Wednesday	Thursday	Friday
_____ Minutes	_____ Minutes	_____ Minutes	_____ Minutes	_____ Minutes

7.2 Two-Step Word Problems: Addition and Subtraction

Name: _____ Date: _____

Read, Write, Solve, and Discover!

Write math sentences and draw pictures to solve two-step word problems.

Daniel sees a symbol on his sheet music. Do you know what it is? Read each word problem. Then fill out and solve the equations using the word problems and pictures. Write your answer on each line. Then use your answers to write the letters on the lines to see the name of the symbol!

Example:

Daniel looks at one page of sheet music that has 45 notes with 5 notes per measure. He has 3 pages of sheet music with the same numbers of notes and measures. How many measures are there in total?

$$45 \div 5 = 9$$

$$9 \times 3 = 27 \quad \text{T}$$

Use any shape for your pictures. Remember to draw 2 pictures, 1 for each equation!

Put a T on the lines that have a 27 under them.

Draw your pictures here:

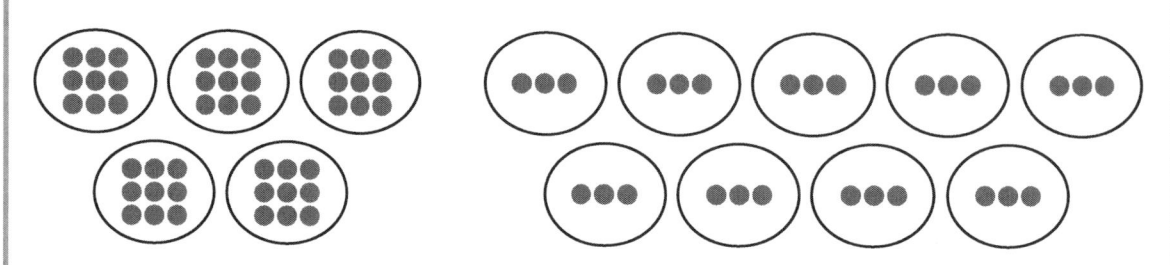

There are __27__ measures in total.

73 7.3 Two-Step Word Problems: Multiplication and Division

Next page

1. Daniel has 4 pages of sheet music. There are 4 notes on each page. The notes are equal groups on 8 measures. How many notes are on each measure?

☐ × ☐ = ☐ | ☐ ÷ ☐ = ☐ E

Draw your pictures here:

There are _____ measures in total.

2. Daniel has 40 pages of sheet music to give to 5 students in equal groups. Each page has 4 notes on it. How many notes will each student have on their sheet music?

☐ ÷ ☐ = ☐ | ☐ × ☐ = ☐ L

Draw your pictures here:

Each student will have _____ notes in total.

7.3 Two-Step Word Problems: Multiplication and Division

3. Daniel has 35 pages of sheet music to give to 7 students in equal groups. Each page has 5 notes on it. How many notes will each student have on their sheet music?

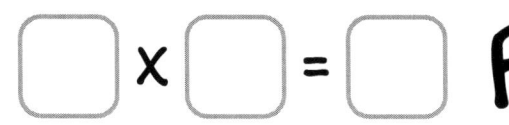

☐ ÷ ☐ = ☐ | ☐ x ☐ = ☐ R

Draw your pictures here:

Each student will have _____ notes on their sheet music.

4. Daniel has 5 pages of sheet music with 4 measures on each page. The sixth page has half of the number of measures as on the other five pages. How many measures are on the sixth page?

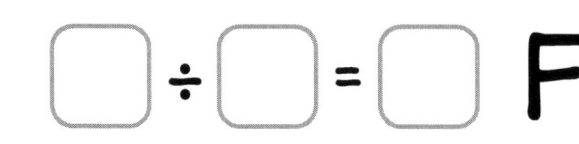

☐ x ☐ = ☐ | ☐ ÷ ☐ = ☐ F

Draw your pictures here:

There are _____ measures on the sixth page.

75   7.3 Two-Step Word Problems: Multiplication and Division

Next page

5. Daniel has a page of sheet music that has 54 notes with 6 notes per measure. He has a second page of sheet music that has double the number of measures as on the first page. How many measures are on the second page?

☐ ÷ ☐ = ☐ | ☐ × ☐ = ☐ B

Draw your pictures here:

There are _____ measures on the second page.

This symbol is a

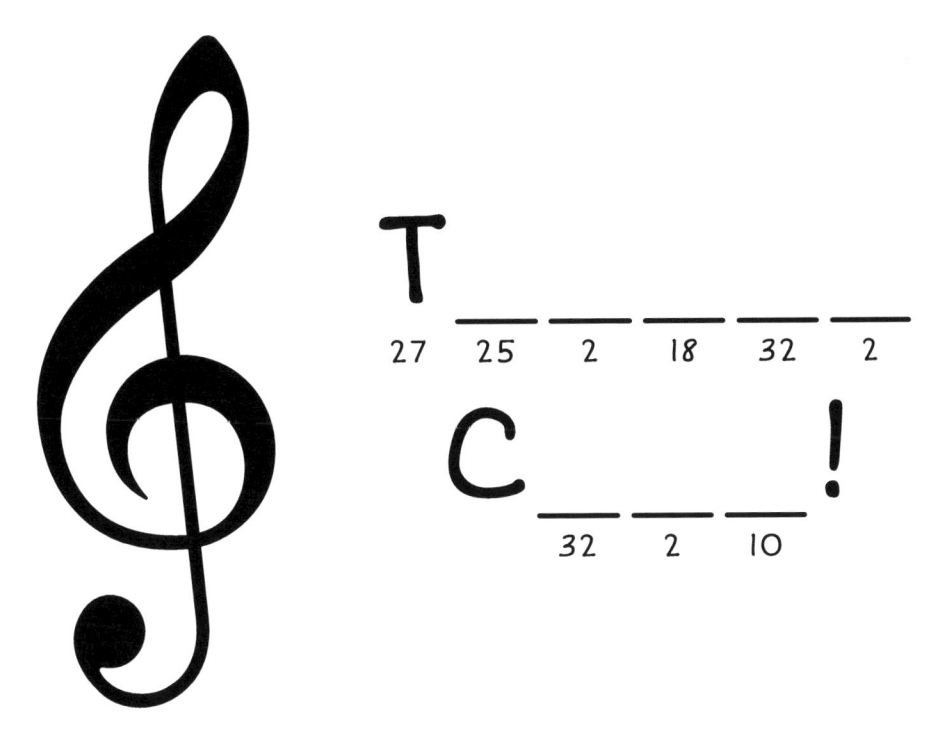

T _ _ _ _ _ _
27 25 2 18 32 2

C _ _ _ !
32 2 10

7.3 Two-Step Word Problems: Multiplication and Division

Name: _____ Date: _____

Read, Write, Solve, and Color!

Write math sentences and draw pictures to solve two-step word problems.

Ava needs your help to keep track of the tickets the class sells. The students want to meet a 110-ticket goal! Read each word problem. Then fill out and solve the equations using the word problems and pictures. Write your answer on each line. Then color the meter to show each of your answers to see if the class will meet their goal!

Example:

The class sells 3 groups of 5 tickets. Then they sell 10 more tickets. How many tickets did they sell in all?

$$3 \times 5 = 15$$

$$15 + 10 = 25$$

Use any shape for your pictures. Remember to draw 2 pictures, 1 for each equation!

Color in 25 on the ticket meter. If you already colored in part of the meter, color 25 more!

10 + 25 = 35

Draw your pictures here:

The class sold __25__ tickets.

77   7.4 Two-Step Word Problems: All Four Operations

Next page

1. The class had 20 tickets. They lost 15 of them. They sold 4 times the amount left over. How many ticket did they sell?

☐ - ☐ = ☐ | ☐ × ☐ = ☐

Draw your pictures here:

They sold _____ tickets.

2. The class had 49 tickets. They gave away 29 tickets. Then the class sold half of the rest of the tickets. How many tickets did they sell?

☐ - ☐ = ☐ | ☐ ÷ ☐ = ☐

Draw your pictures here:

They sold _____ tickets.

7.4 Two-Step Word Problems: All Four Operations

3. The class sold 3 piles of 8 tickets. Then they sold 6 more tickets. How many tickets did they sell altogether?

☐ × ☐ = ☐ | ☐ + ☐ = ☐

Draw your pictures here:

They sold _____ tickets.

4. The class had 18 tickets and sold half of them. Then they sold 41 more tickets. How many tickets did they sell in total?

☐ ÷ ☐ = ☐ | ☐ + ☐ = ☐

Draw your pictures here:

The class sold _____ tickets in total.

7.4 Two-Step Word Problems: All Four Operations

Tickets Sold

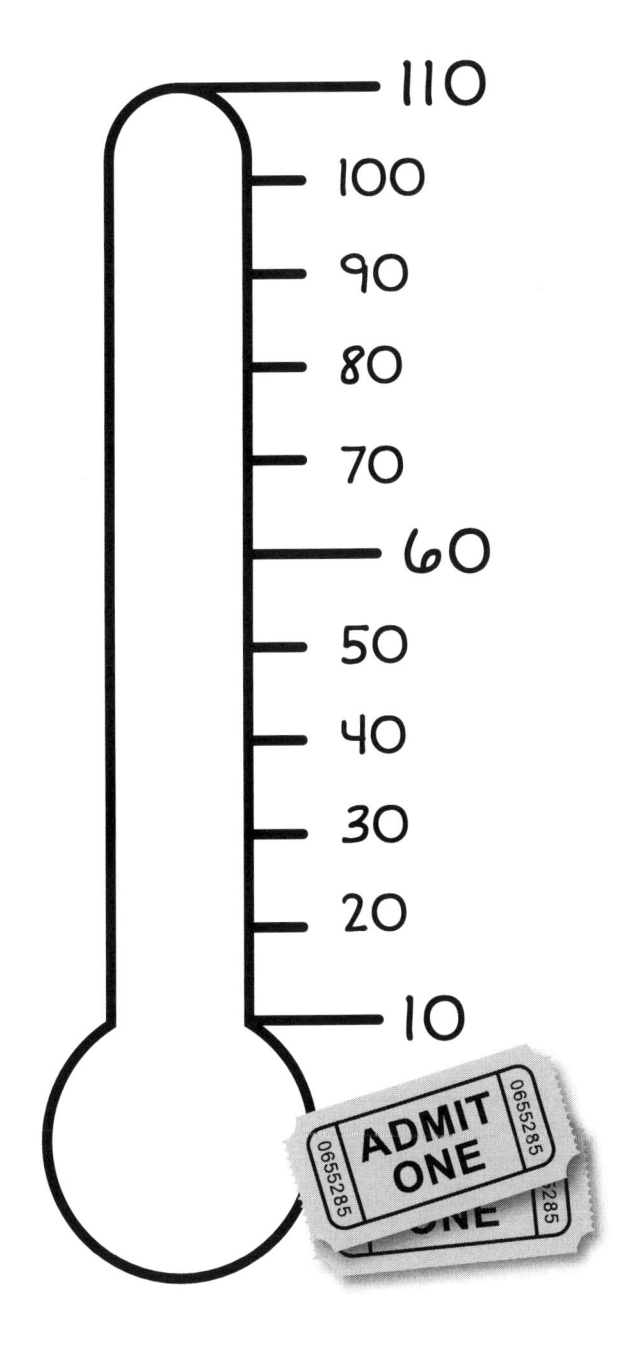

110
100
90
80
70
60
50
40
30
20
10

7.4 Two-Step Word Problems: All Four Operations

Name: _____ Date: _____

Make and Color!

Make even or odd numbers by adding or subtracting.

Madelyn needs your help to organize the snacks! First, read the problem. Then, circle the correct number to write in the addition or subtraction sentence to solve the problem. Write the digits of your answer in the boxes. In the picture below, color your even answers in orange, your odd answers in purple, and any numbers that are not answers in blue. You will make a picture of healthy snacks!

Example:
Madelyn needs an odd number of apple chips.

35 is an odd answer. Find it on the picture and color those spaces red.

$$67 - 32 = 35$$

(32) 31

1. Madelyn needs an even number of pieces of broccoli.

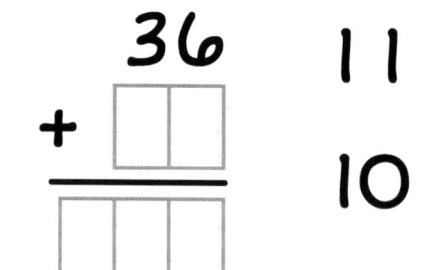

$$36 + \square\square = \square\square$$

11
10

2. Madelyn needs an odd number of bottles of water.

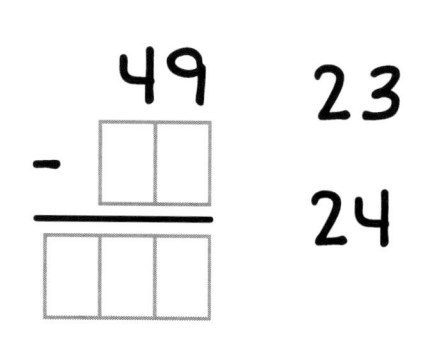

$$49 - \square\square = \square\square$$

23
24

3. Madelyn needs an even number of apple chips.

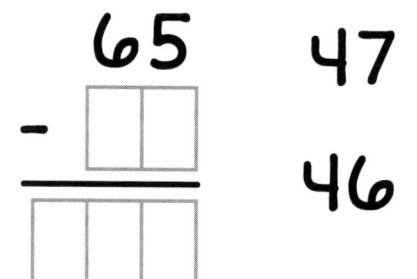

$$65 - \square\square = \square\square$$

47
46

81

8.1 Even and Odd Numbers

Next page

4. Madelyn needs an odd number of carrot sticks.

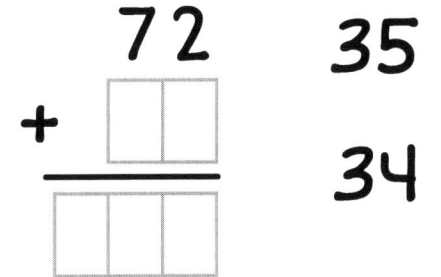

$$72 + \square\square = \square\square\square$$

35

34

5. Madelyn needs an odd number of pieces of pepper.

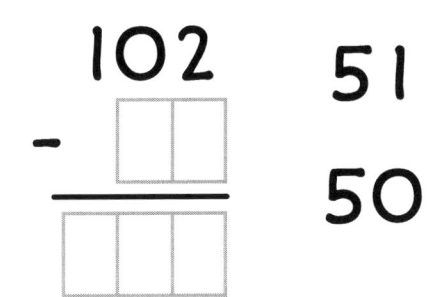

$$102 - \square\square = \square\square\square$$

51

50

6. Challenge

Is the product of 2 × 5 an even number or an odd number? Think about repeated addition and multiplication! Then write or draw to show why the product would be even or odd.

Even number

Odd number

Any other number

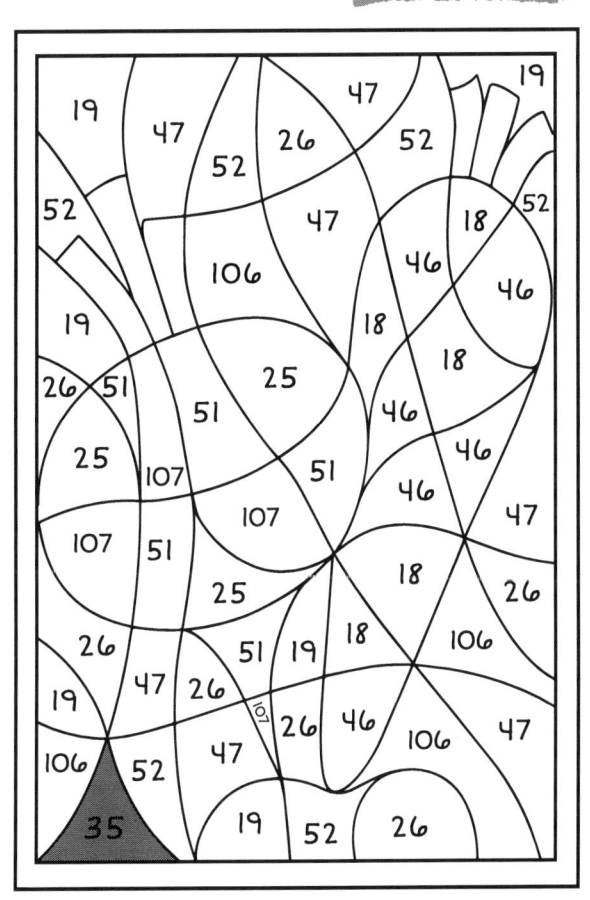

8.1 Even and Odd Numbers

Name: _____ Date: _____

Add and Color!
Use addition table patterns to solve addition equations.

Zoe wants to add more calories! Circle the addition table patterns that you use to find each answer. Write the answer you find on the line after each =. Color the correct box in the addition table for each answer.

Example:

(even + even)   odd + odd   odd + even

(number + 0) (number + 10)

0 + 10 = 10

Find the 10 where 0 and 10 meet on the addition table and color it in!

+	1	2	3	4	5	6	7	8	9	10
1	2	3	4	5	6	7	8	9	10	11
2	3	4	5	6	7	8	9	10	11	12
3	4	5	6	7	8	9	10	11	12	13
4	5	6	7	8	9	10	11	12	13	14
5	6	7	8	9	10	11	12	13	14	15
6	7	8	9	10	11	12	13	14	15	16
7	8	9	10	11	12	13	14	15	16	17
8	9	10	11	12	13	14	15	16	17	18
9	10	11	12	13	14	15	16	17	18	19
10	11	12	13	14	15	16	17	18	19	20

8.3 Addition Table Patterns

Next page

1.

even + even   odd + odd   odd + even

number + 0   number + 10

5 + 0 = ☐

2.

even + even   odd + odd   odd + even

number + 0   number + 10

6 + 6 = ☐

3.

even + even   odd + odd   odd + even

number + 0   number + 10

10 + 8 = ☐

4.

even + even   odd + odd   odd + even

number + 0   number + 10

8 + 9 = ☐

8.3 Addition Table Patterns

5.

even + even   odd + odd   odd + even

number + 0   number + 10

9 + 7 = ☐

Challenge: Would the sum of 10 + 11 be an even or an odd number? Circle the pattern you would use to find out!

even + even   odd + odd   odd + even

number + 0   number + 10

10 + 11 = 21

Name: _____ Date: _____

Multiply, Color, and Write!

Use multiplication table patterns to solve multiplication equations.

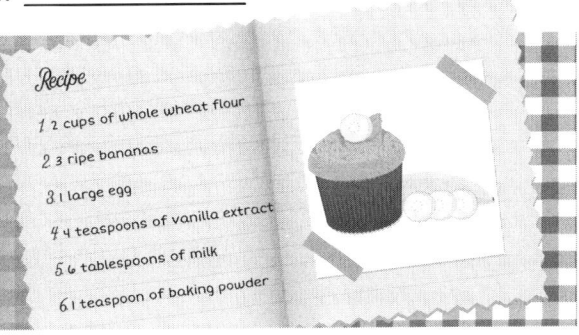

Recipe
1. 2 cups of whole wheat flour
2. 3 ripe bananas
3. 1 large egg
4. 4 teaspoons of vanilla extract
5. 6 tablespoons of milk
6. 1 teaspoon of baking powder

Logan wants to make a new recipe for a big batch of muffins! Use the multiplication table to find each answer. Circle one or more of the multiplication table patterns you use to find the answer. Write the answer you find on the line after each = and color it on the table. Then write each answer next to the correct ingredient in Logan's recipe.

Example: cups of oil

even + even   odd + odd   (odd + even)

number x 2   number x 5   number x 10

$$5 \times 10 = \boxed{50}$$

> Find where the 5 and 10 meet on the multiplication table and color it in! Then write "50" next to "cups of oil"!

X	1	2	3	4	5	6	7	8	9	10
1	1	2	3	4	5	6	7	8	9	10
2	2	4	6	8	10	12	14	16	18	20
3	3	6	9	12	15	18	21	24	27	30
4	4	8	12	16	20	24	28	32	36	40
5	5	10	15	20	25	30	35	40	45	50
6	6	12	18	24	30	36	42	48	54	60
7	7	14	21	28	35	42	49	56	63	70
8	8	16	24	32	40	48	56	64	72	80
9	9	18	27	36	45	54	63	72	81	90
10	10	20	30	40	50	60	70	80	90	100

8.4 Multiplication Table Patterns

Next page

1. cups of whole wheat flour

　　even + even　　odd + odd　　odd + even

　　number x 2　　number x 5　　number x 10

$$4 \times 8 = \boxed{}$$

2. ripe bananas

　　even + even　　odd + odd　　odd + even

　　number x 2　　number x 5　　number x 10

$$9 \times 5 = \boxed{}$$

3. large eggs

　　even + even　　odd + odd　　odd + even

　　number x 2　　number x 5　　number x 10

$$10 \times 1 = \boxed{}$$

4. teaspoons of vanilla extract

　　even + even　　odd + odd　　odd + even

　　number x 2　　number x 5　　number x 10

$$6 \times 4 = \boxed{}$$

8.4 Multiplication Table Patterns

5. tablespoons of milk

    even + even   odd + odd   odd + even

    number x 2   number x 5   number x 10

$$7 \times 7 = \boxed{}$$

6. teaspoons of baking powder

    even + even   odd + odd   odd + even

    number x 2   number x 5   number x 10

$$2 \times 8 = \boxed{}$$

Recipe

1. **50** cups of oil
2. ___ cups of whole wheat flour
3. ___ ripe bananas
4. ___ large eggs
5. ___ teaspoons of vanilla extract
6. ___ tablepoons of milk
7. ___ teaspoons of baking powder

8.4 Multiplication Table Patterns

Name: _____ Date: _____

Solve and Discover!

Decompose or adjust numbers to solve addition and subtraction equations.

Look at the numbers in each equation. Fill out the lines below the equations to decompose or adjust the numbers to solve. Write your answer in each box. Then use your answers to write the letters on the lines and see a hidden message about healthy food!

Example: Adjust the addends to find the sum.

$790 - 545 = ?$ Y

-1 -1

$789 - 544 =$ ☐ 245

Find the number 245 in the hidden message. Write the letter Y on the line.

1. Decompose each addend to find the sum.

$376 + 23 = ?$ H

___ + ___ + ___ + ___ + ___ = ?

___ + ___ + ___ = ☐

89   8.5 Decomposing and Adjusting to Solve

Next page

2. Adjust each addend to find the sum.

$$628 + 154 = ?$$ A

___ + __ + ___ = ?

___ + ___ = ☐

3. Decompose the minuend and the subtrahend to find the difference.

$$587 - 232 = ?$$

    ___ + ___ + ___   T

− ___ + ___ + ___
─────────────────

    ___ + ___ + ___ = ☐

4. Adjust each addend to find the sum.

$$891 + 465 = ?$$ N

− ___   − ___

___ + ___ = ☐

8.5 Decomposing and Adjusting to Solve

90

Challenge: Ava needs your help! She tried to adjust to subtract, but she did not get the correct difference. Circle where Ava made a mistake. Then write the correct number on the line below.

$$950 - 639 = ?$$
$$-1 \quad -1$$
$$949 - 639 = \boxed{310}$$

N

_____

_ E _ L _ _ Y _ _ D S _ RO _ G
399   762   355 399 245   782 426   355   426

Name: _____ Date: _____

Solve and Write!
Use the commutative property and arrays to solve multiplication sentences.

Caleb wants to make a list of all of the tickets the class needs. Solve each multiplication equation using the commutative property. Then, create an array using the grids to check your answers. Look for the picture of the ride next to your answer. Finally, write that answer next to the correct picture on Caleb's list!

Example: 2 × 7 = 14
7 × 2 = 14

You will put a 14 next to the Ferris wheel on Caleb's list!

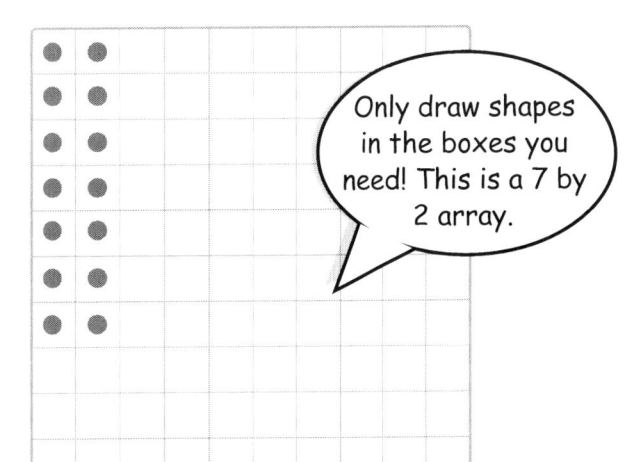

Only draw shapes in the boxes you need! This is a 7 by 2 array.

1.
9 × 3 = 27
3 × 9 = ☐

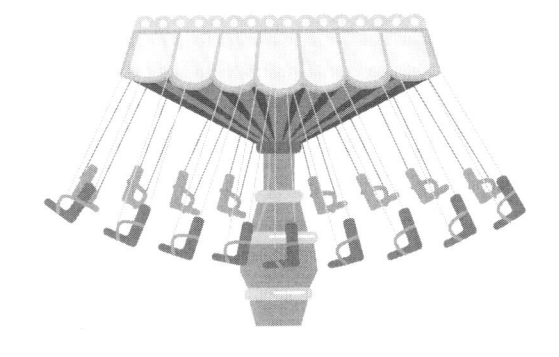

9.1 The Commutative Property of Multiplication

2.

$4 \times 6 = 24$

$6 \times 4 = \boxed{}$

3.

$8 \times 5 = 40$

$5 \times 8 = \boxed{}$

9.1 The Commutative Property of Multiplication

Next page

4.
$7 \times 10 = 70$
$10 \times 7 = \boxed{}$

CLASS TICKET LIST

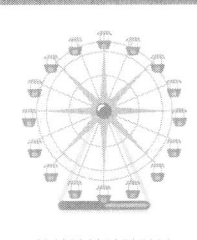

__14__ tickets

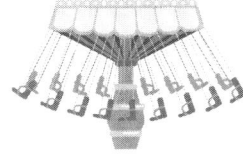

_____ tickets

_____ tickets

_____ tickets

_____ tickets

9.1 The Commutative Property of Multiplication

Name: _____ Date: _____

Solve and Color!

Use the associative property to solve multiplication sentences.

Daniel wants to win a special prize at the Kick a Goal! game. Find the product of the grouped factors. Then, write both factors on the lines below each multiplication sentence. Find the total product using any method that works for you, and write it in the box. Then, find your answer on pieces of the picture. Color those pieces the color shown next to the multiplication sentence to see the special prize!

Example:

$(4 \times 5) \times 2 = ?$

$\underline{20} \times \underline{2} = \boxed{40}$

PINK

Color pink the parts of the picture that have 40 on them.

1.

$7 \times (2 \times 2) = ?$

$\underline{} \times \underline{} = \boxed{}$

BLUE

2.

$(3 \times 2) \times 5 = ?$

$\underline{} \times \underline{} = \boxed{}$

YELLOW

95

9.3 The Associative Property of Multiplication

Next page

3.

(3 x 3) x 5 = ?

___ x ___ = ☐

RED

4.

9 x (2 x 5) = ?

___ x ___ = ☐

GRAY

Challenge: Can you find the two ways to group the factors using the associative property? Use parentheses to group one set of factors and then the other. Solve both equations to see if you get the same product!

3 x 3 x 2 = ?

___ x ___ = ☐

3 x 3 x 2 = ?

___ x ___ = ☐

9.3 The Associative Property of Multiplication

Color by Numbers

97   9.3 The Associative Property of Multiplication

Name: _____ Date: _____

Jump, Find, Write!
Use a number line to find a missing factor in a multiplication equation.

Circle the product of each multiplication sentence on the number line underneath it. Then, make jumps to find each missing factor. Do not forget to switch the factors if you need to! Write your answers in the boxes. Look for the letter next to each problem. Then, use your answers to write the letters on the lines and see the name of a tasty snack!

Example:

Switch the factors if the second factor is missing!

$7 \times \boxed{2} = 14$ **F**

$? \times \underline{7} = \boxed{14}$

Put a F on the lines that have a 2 under them.

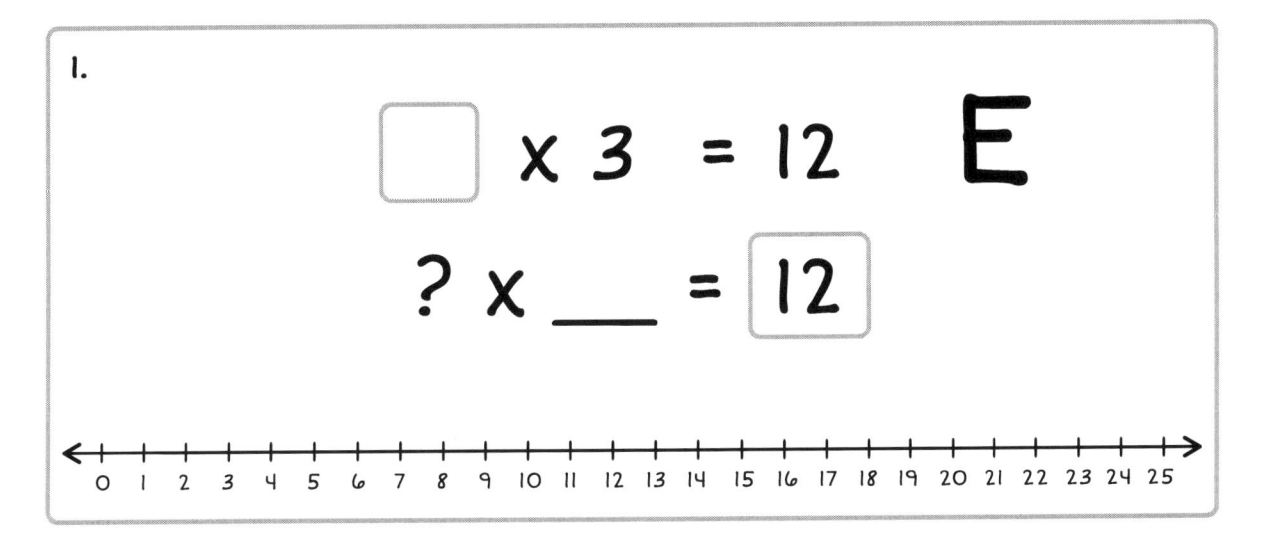

← 0 1 2 3 4 5 6 7 8 9 10 11 12 13 ⑭ 15 16 17 18 19 20 21 22 23 24 25 →

1.

$\boxed{} \times 3 = 12$ **E**

$? \times \underline{} = \boxed{12}$

← 0 1 2 3 4 5 6 7 8 9 10 11 12 13 14 15 16 17 18 19 20 21 22 23 24 25 →

9.4 Missing Factors

2.

$$5 \times \boxed{} = 25$$

$$? \times \underline{} = \boxed{25}$$

A

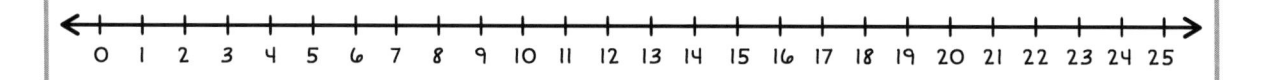

←+—+→
0 1 2 3 4 5 6 7 8 9 10 11 12 13 14 15 16 17 18 19 20 21 22 23 24 25

3.

$$\boxed{} \times 2 = 16$$

$$? \times \underline{} = \boxed{16}$$

N

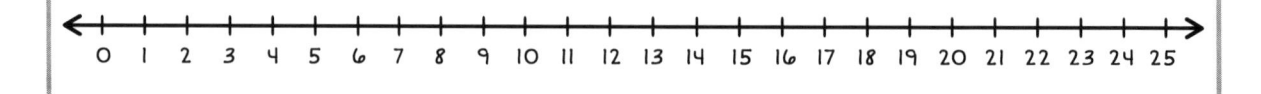

←+—+→
0 1 2 3 4 5 6 7 8 9 10 11 12 13 14 15 16 17 18 19 20 21 22 23 24 25

4.

$$8 \times \boxed{} = 24$$

$$? \times \underline{} = \boxed{24}$$

K

←+—+→
0 1 2 3 4 5 6 7 8 9 10 11 12 13 14 15 16 17 18 19 20 21 22 23 24 25

9.4 Missing Factors

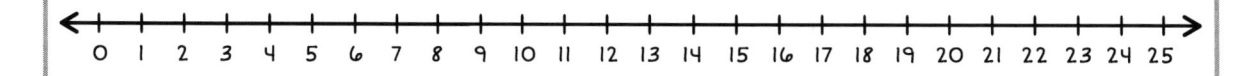

Next page

Challenge: Can you find a missing factor using a number line that does not count by ones? The number line below counts by 2s. Can you find the missing factor using the same steps? Circle the product. Make jumps that are as far apart as the factor you have. Think about how many 2s you need to make each jump! Write the number of jumps you make in the box.

☐ x 4 = 28

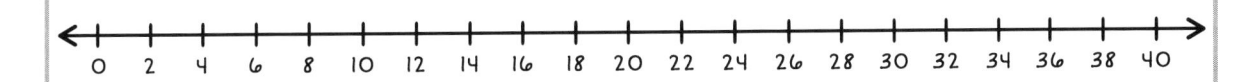

0 2 4 6 8 10 12 14 16 18 20 22 24 26 28 30 32 34 36 38 40

F U __ __ __ L C __ __ __
2   8 8 4   5 3 4

9.4 Missing Factors

Name: _____ Date: _____

Write and Match!

Fill out input/output tables to solve multiplication equations.

Can you help Logan count the gifts in the gift shop? Use the patterns and/or multiplication sentences to fill out each table. Then, draw a line to connect each table to an equation that can be solved using the table. Write the product in the box before each gift.

Example:

Input	Output
1	4
2	8
3	12
4	16
5	20
6	24
7	28
8	32

Rule: x 4

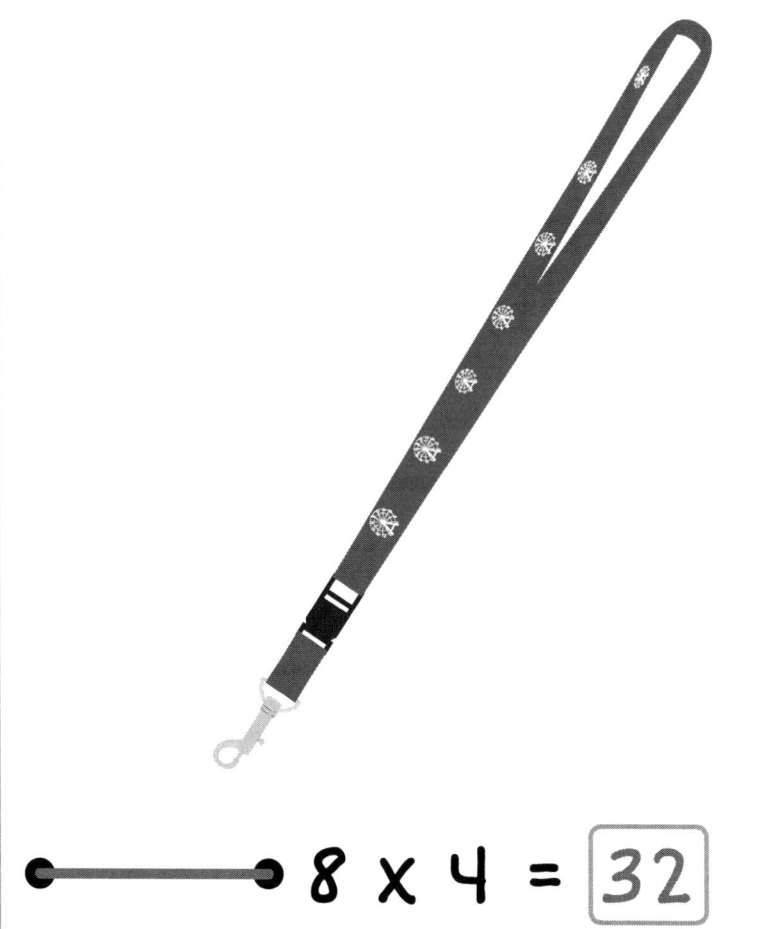

$8 \times 4 = \boxed{32}$

101

9.5 Multiplication Input and Output Tables

Next page

Input	1	2	3	4				
Output	5	10			25	30	35	40

Rule: x 5

7 x 2 = ☐

Input	Output
	2
	4
	6
4	
5	
6	12
7	
	16

Rule: x 2

6 x 10 = ☐

Input	1					
Output	10	20	30	40		

Rule: x 10

5 x 5 = ☐

9.5 Multiplication Input and Output Tables

Challenge: Logan's teacher wants to buy 5 coffee mugs. Each coffee mug costs $4. How much will it cost for Logan's teacher to buy the coffee mugs? Fill out the input/output table below. Then, write and solve a multiplication sentence using the table.

# of Mugs	Cost
1	4

Rule: x 4

☐ x ☐ = ☐

Name: _____ Date: _____

Use a Multiplication Strategy!

Use what you know about multiplication strategies to answer the questions.

Find the product of each multiplication sentence using the given strategy.

Example: Solve this question using a number line.

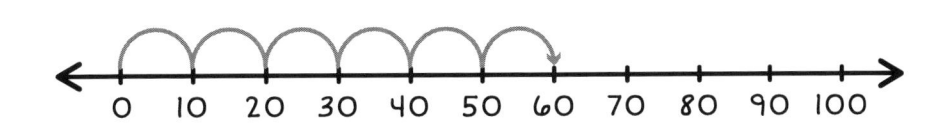

$$\begin{array}{r} 6 \\ \times\ 10 \\ \hline 60 \end{array}$$

0 10 20 30 40 50 60 70 80 90 100

1. Solve this question using an array.

   7 x 7 = ☐

10.1 Multiplication Strategies Within 100

2. Solve this question using skip counting.

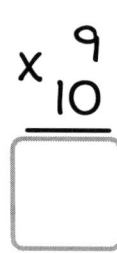

$$\times \begin{array}{r} 9 \\ 10 \\ \hline \square \end{array}$$

__ __ __ __ __ __ __ __ __ __

3. Solve this question using a multiplication table.

$7 \times 9 = \square$

x	1	2	3	4	5	6	7	8	9	10
1	1	2	3	4	5	6	7	8	9	10
2	2	4	6	8	10	12	14	16	18	20
3	3	6	9	12	15	18	21	24	27	30
4	4	8	12	16	20	24	28	32	36	40
5	5	10	15	20	25	30	35	40	45	50
6	6	12	18	24	30	36	42	48	54	60
7	7	14	21	28	35	42	49	56	63	70
8	8	16	24	32	40	48	56	64	72	80
9	9	18	27	36	45	54	63	72	81	90
10	10	20	30	40	50	60	70	80	90	100

4. Solve this question using repeated addition.

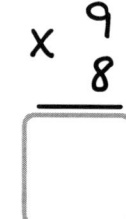

$$\times \begin{array}{r} 9 \\ 8 \\ \hline \square \end{array}$$

__ + __ + __ + __ + __ + __ + __ + __ + __ = __

5. Solve this question using a number line.

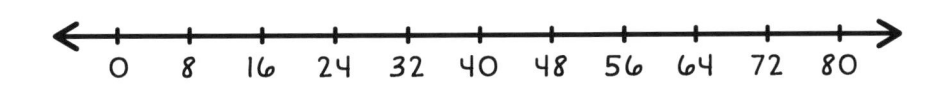

$$10 \times 8 = \boxed{}$$

←—+—+—+—+—+—+—+—+—+—+—→
0   8 16 24 32 40 48 56 64 72 80

6. Solve this question by drawing a picture.

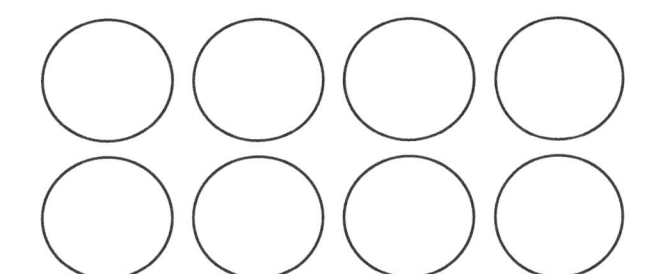

$$\begin{array}{r} 8 \\ \times\ 6 \\ \hline \end{array}$$

○ ○ ○ ○
○ ○ ○ ○

10.1 Multiplication Strategies Within 100

Name: _____ Date: _____

Draw a Picture!

Read each multiplication word problem. Write an equation and find the product by drawing a picture.

Example: Solve this question by drawing a picture.

$$6 \times 6 = 36$$

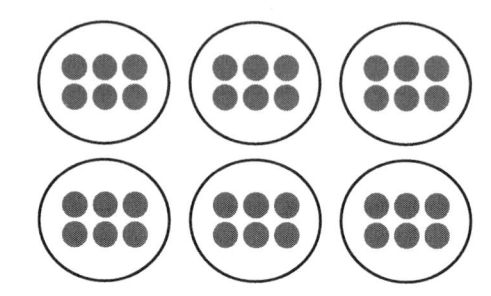

1. An ostrich picks 8 leaves off 6 different trees. How many leaves does the ostrich pick in total?

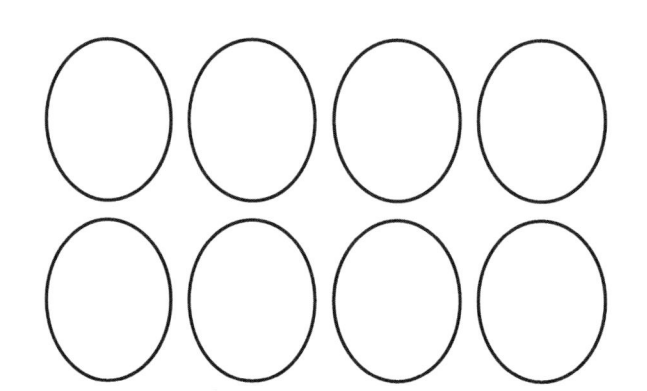

107 10.2 Represent Word Problems Using Pictures and Equations

Next page

2. 10 dolphins each jump through 10 hoops. How many jumps do the dolphins do altogether?

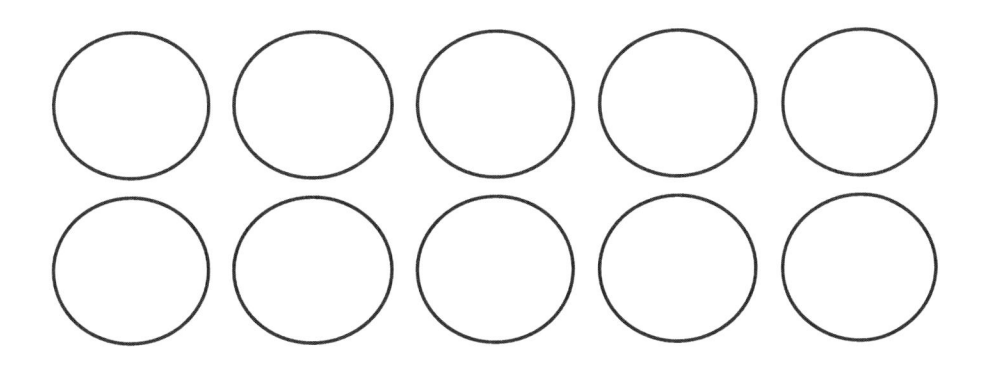

3. A rabbit digs 9 holes every day for 8 days. How many holes does it dig in total?

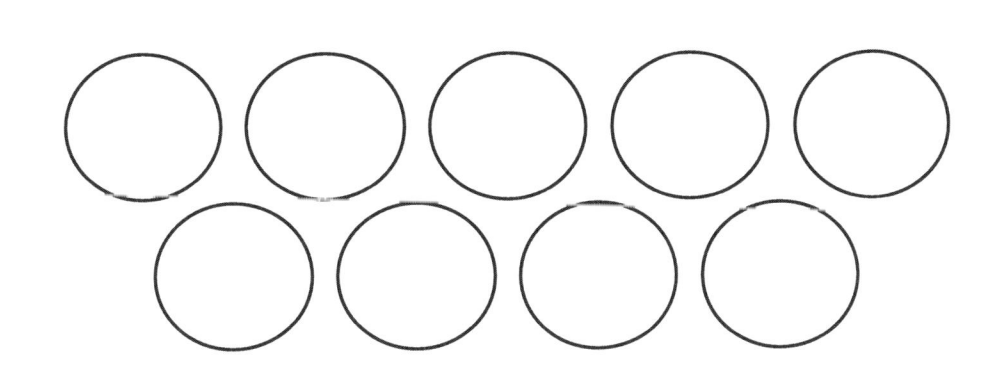

10.2 Represent Word Problems Using Pictures and Equations

4. 7 lions each have 6 toy balls. How many toy balls do the lions have altogether?

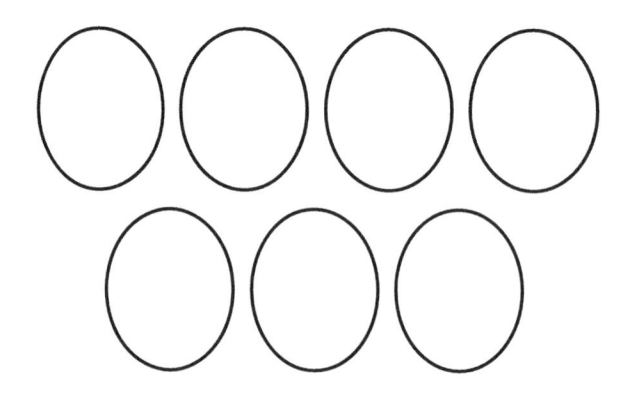

5. 8 zookeepers each hold 10 birds. How many birds do they hold in total?

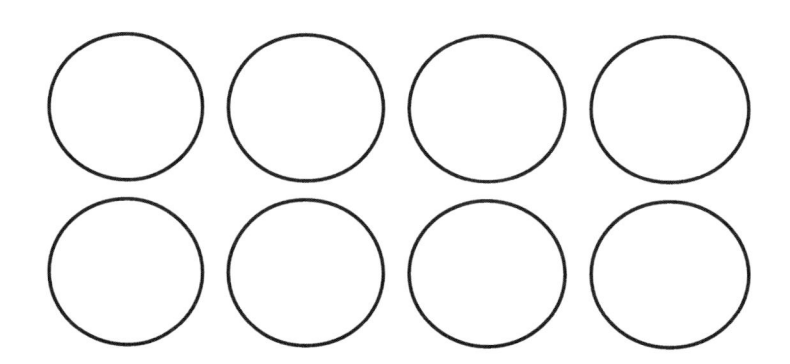

Name: _____ Date: _____

Zoo Multiplication
Read the word problems. Use a grid to make an array. Find the product.

1. There are 9 monkeys at the zoo. Each monkey eats 6 bananas. How many bananas did the monkeys eat?

    9 × 6 = ☐

2. There are 7 monkeys at the zoo. Each monkey eats 6 bananas. How many bananas do the monkeys eat?

    7 × 6 = ☐

10.3 Solve Multiplication Situations and Quantities

110
Next page

3. There were 10 people in line waiting to see the gorillas. If each ticket costs 7 dollars, how much money do the people spend altogether?

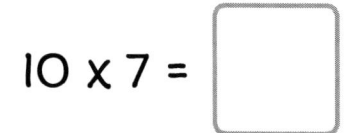

10 x 7 = ☐

4. An alligator eats 8 fish in a minute. How many fish can the alligator eat in 8 minutes?

8 x 8 = ☐

Name: _____ Date: _____

What's the Number?

Find each unknown number using multiplication or a related division fact. Show your work using the strategies listed in each box. Then write the unknown number in the box.

Example:

Multiplication Equation

7 x ? = 56

Strategy: Array

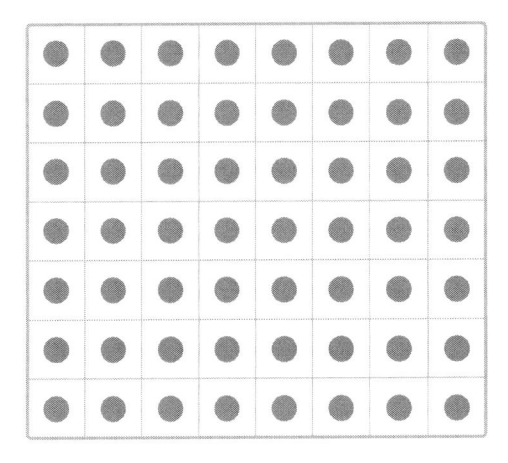

Multiplication or Related Fact

56 ÷ 7 = ?

Unknown Number

8

Example:

Multiplication Equation

6 x 10 = ?

Strategy: Skip Counting

10, 20, 30, 40, 50, 60

Multiplication or Related Fact

6 x 10 = ?

Unknown Number

60

10.5 Multiplication: Missing Numbers

1. **Multiplication Equation**

$? \times 8 = 72$

Strategy: Number Line

Multiplication or Related Fact

[ ]

Unknown Number

[ ]

2. **Multiplication Equation**

$? \times 6 = 48$

Strategy: Division Picture

Multiplication or Related Fact

[ ]

Unknown Number

[ ]

---

3. **Multiplication Equation**

$6 \times ? = 42$

Strategy: Repeated Subtraction

Multiplication or Related Fact

[ ]

Unknown Number

[ ]

4. **Multiplication Equation**

$$7 \times ? = 63$$

Strategy: Equal Groups

Multiplication or Related Fact

Unknown Number

---

5. **Multiplication Equation**

$$10 \times 9 = ?$$

Strategy: Multiplication Table

X	1	2	3	4	5	6	7	8	9	10
1	1	2	3	4	5	6	7	8	9	10
2	2	4	6	8	10	12	14	16	18	20
3	3	6	9	12	15	18	21	24	27	30
4	4	8	12	16	20	24	28	32	36	40
5	5	10	15	20	25	30	35	40	45	50
6	6	12	18	24	30	36	42	48	54	60
7	7	14	21	28	35	42	49	56	63	70
8	8	16	24	32	40	48	56	64	72	80
9	9	18	27	36	45	54	63	72	81	90
10	10	20	30	40	50	60	70	80	90	100

Multiplication or Related Fact

Unknown Number

Name: _____ Date: _____

Move It Away!

Use what you know about division strategies to find the quotients. Use all four strategies. Show your work by drawing or writing each strategy in the blanks below.

Example:

Array

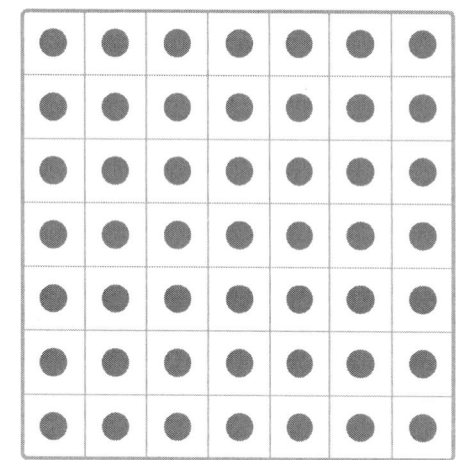

Repeated Subtraction

49-7-7-7-7-7-7-7 = 0

$$49 \div 7 = 7$$

Picture

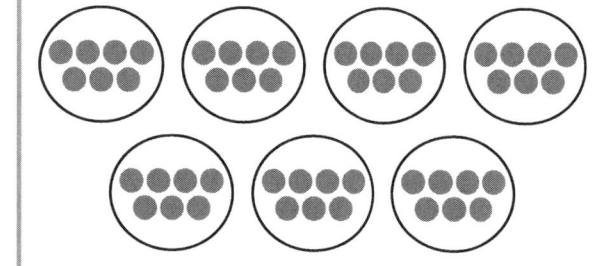

Equal Groups

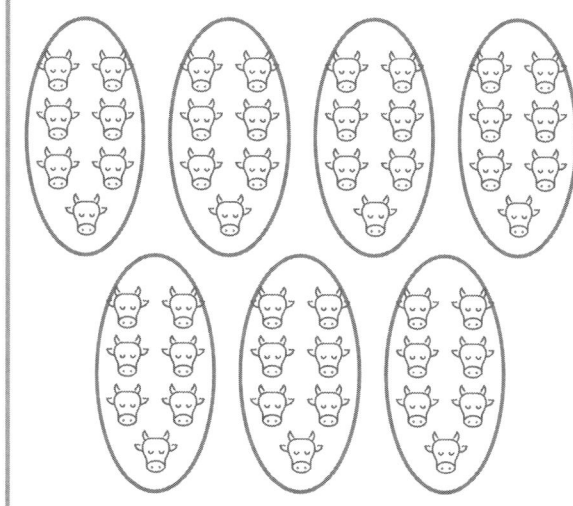

Array

Repeated Subtraction

72 ÷ 8 =

Picture

Equal Groups

11.1 Division Strategies Within 100

116

Next page

Array

Repeated Subtraction

$63 \div 9 =$

Picture

Equal Groups

11.1 Division Strategies Within 100

Name: _____ Date: _____

Division Plants

Let's grow a garden! Read each division word problem. Draw the picture and equation on each plant.

Example:

Equation

$\underline{36} ÷ \underline{6} = \underline{6}$

Picture

There are a total of 36 seeds in Emma's watermelon slices. There are 6 seeds in each slice. How many slices of watermelon did Emma eat?

11.2 Represent Division Word Problems Using Pictures and Equations

1.

Equation

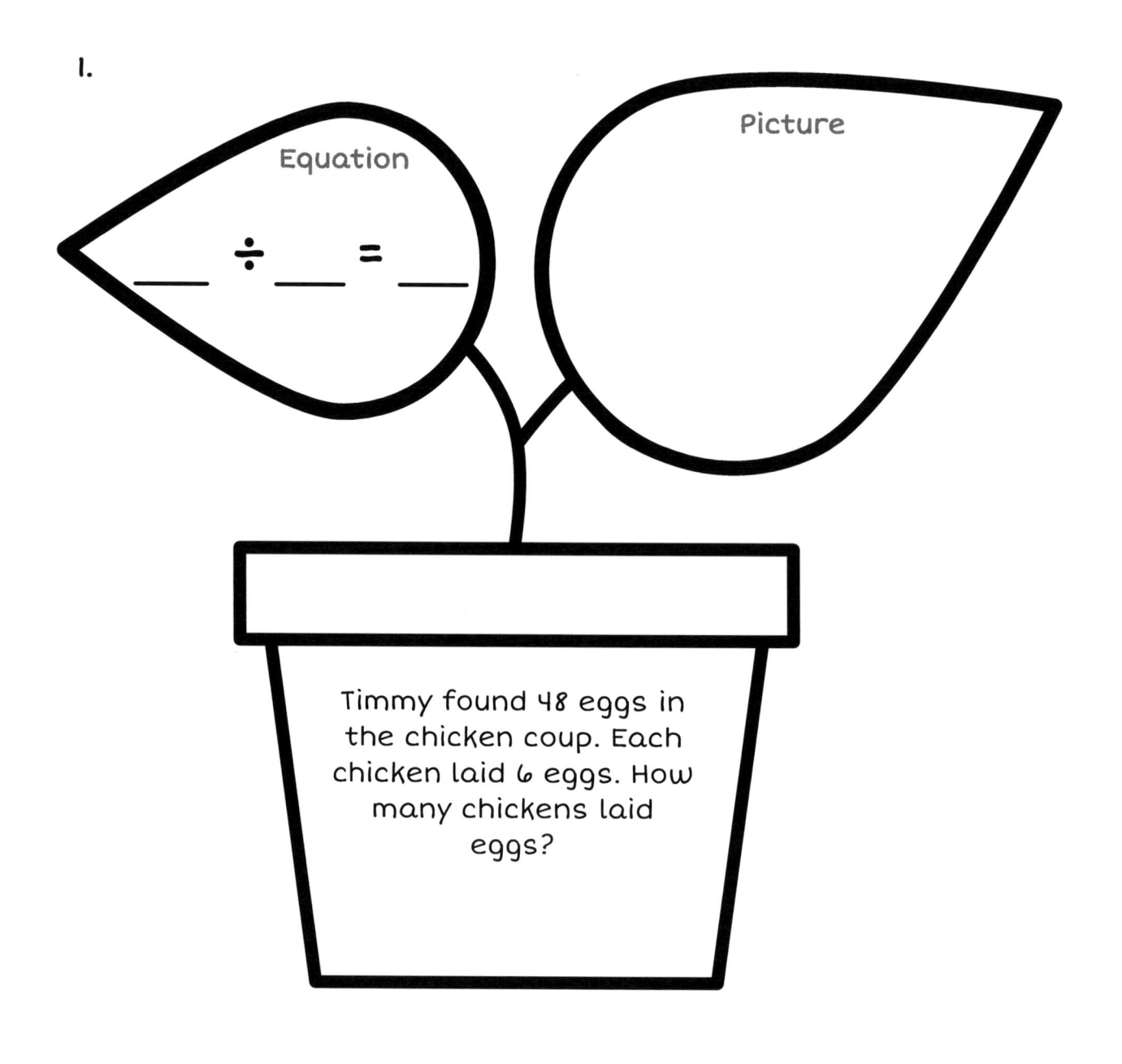

___ ÷ ___ = ___

Picture

Timmy found 48 eggs in the chicken coup. Each chicken laid 6 eggs. How many chickens laid eggs?

11.2 Represent Division Word Problems Using Pictures and Equations

2.

Equation

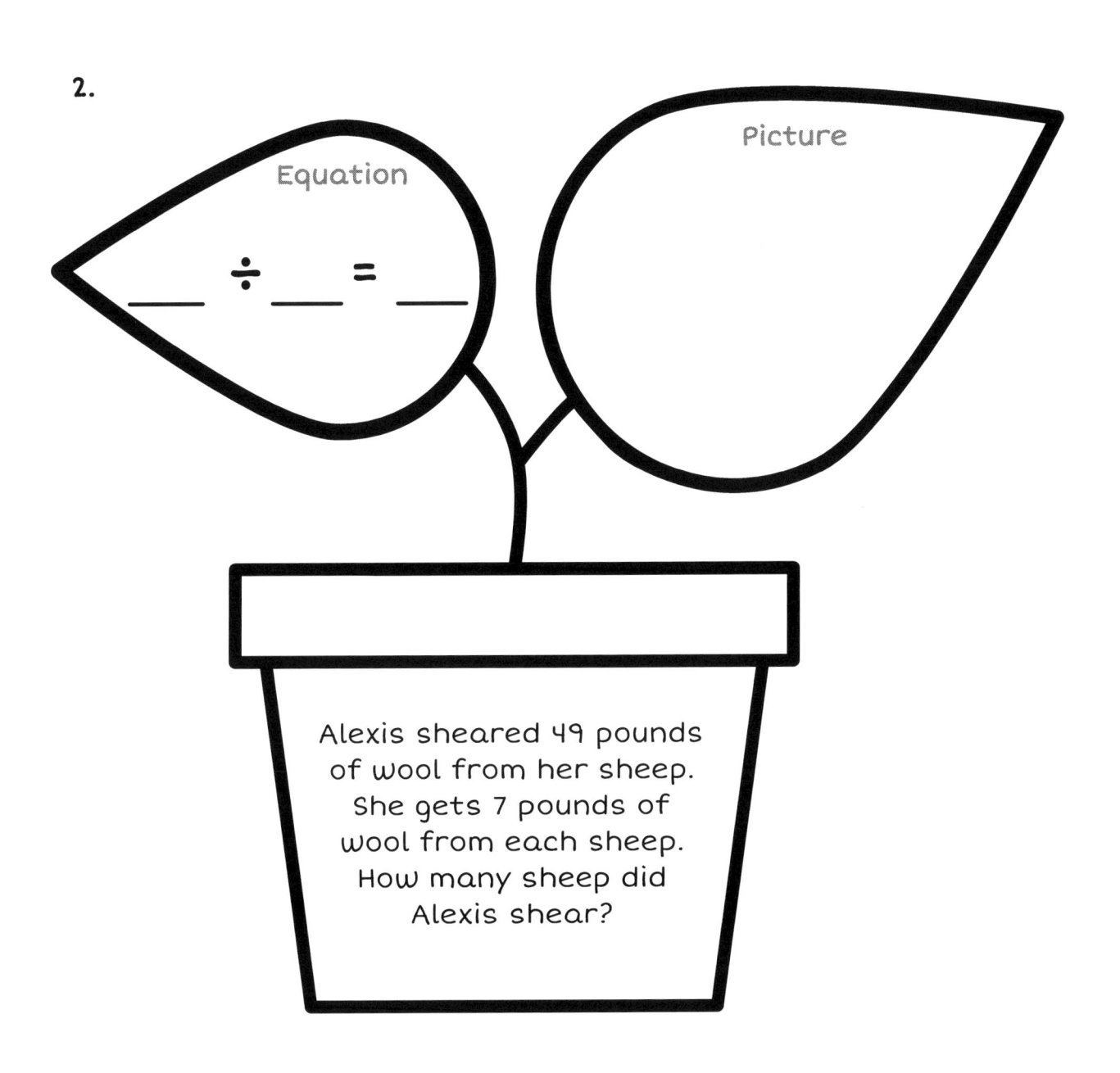

___ ÷ ___ = ___

Picture

Alexis sheared 49 pounds of wool from her sheep. She gets 7 pounds of wool from each sheep. How many sheep did Alexis shear?

11.2 Represent Division Word Problems Using Pictures and Equations

3.

Equation

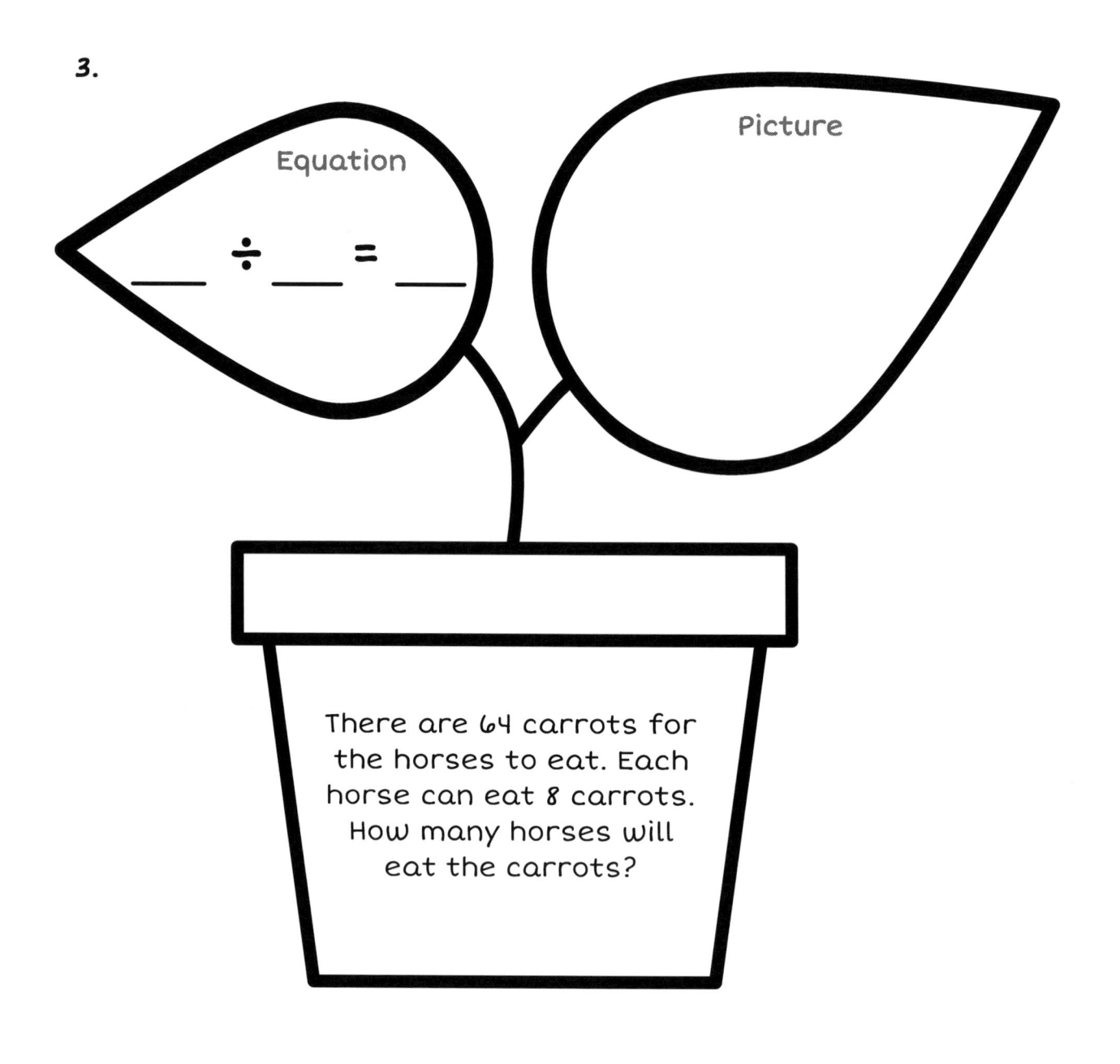

___ ÷ ___ = ___

Picture

There are 64 carrots for the horses to eat. Each horse can eat 8 carrots. How many horses will eat the carrots?

121   11.2 Represent Division Word Problems Using Pictures and Equations

4.

Equation

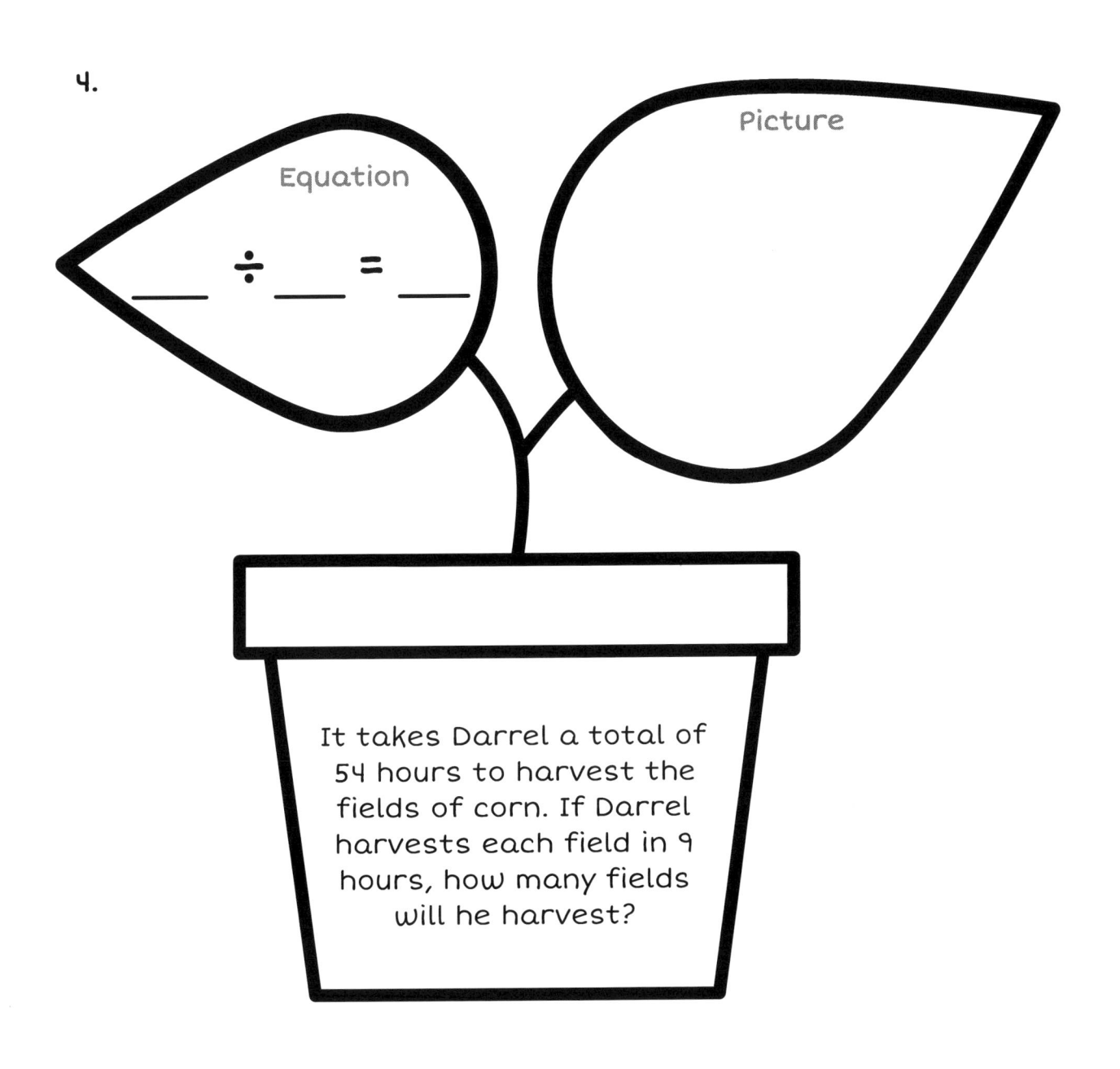

___ ÷ ___ = ___

Picture

It takes Darrel a total of 54 hours to harvest the fields of corn. If Darrel harvests each field in 9 hours, how many fields will he harvest?

11.2 Represent Division Word Problems Using Pictures and Equations

5.

Equation

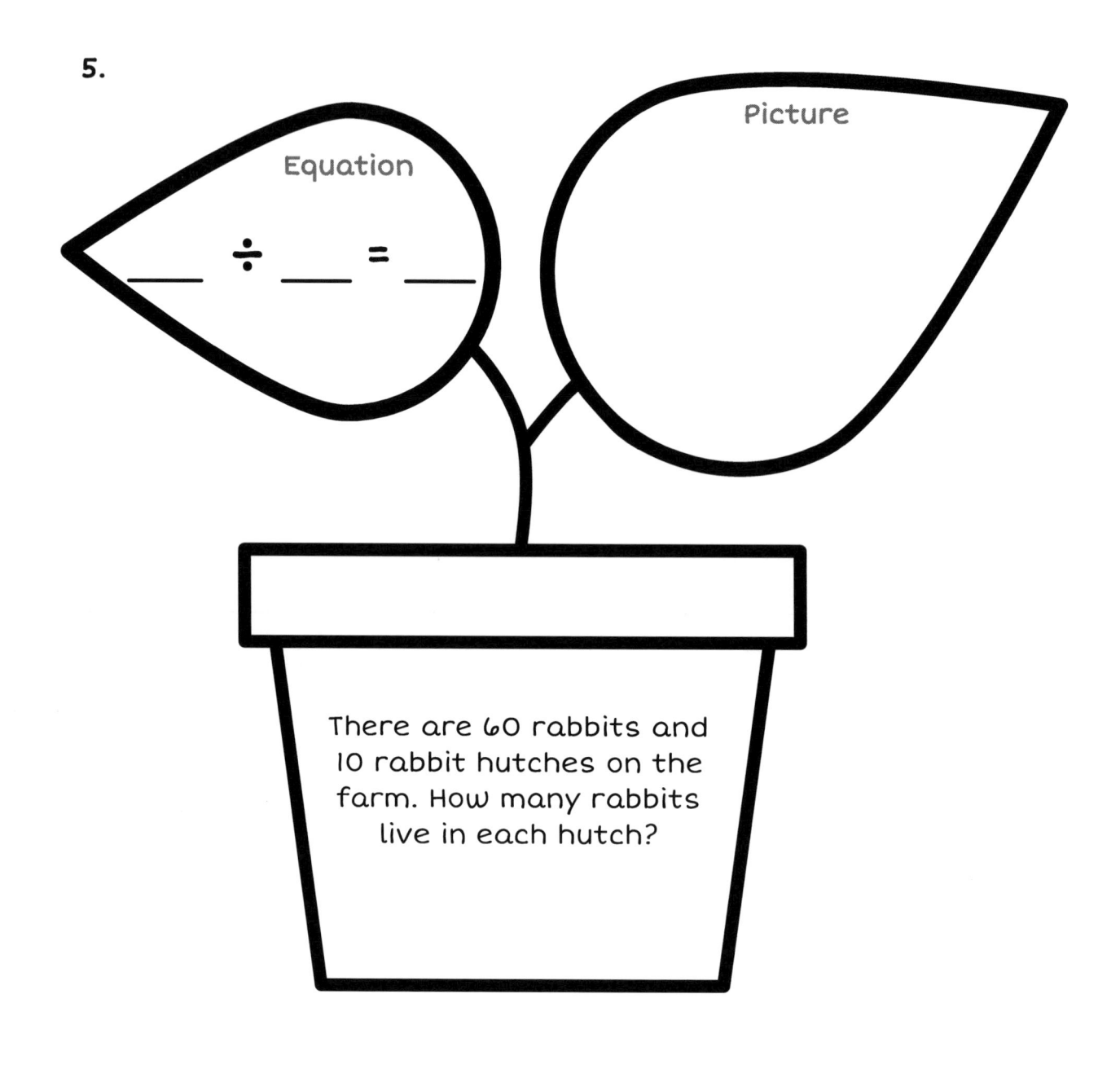

___ ÷ ___ = ___

Picture

There are 60 rabbits and 10 rabbit hutches on the farm. How many rabbits live in each hutch?

Name: _____ Date: _____

Find the Quotient
Use what you know about division pictures and arrays to find the quotient.

Example:

Word Problem
Julia had 64 chickens. She gave 8 chickens to each of her friends. How many friends did Julia give chickens to?

Picture

Equation
$\underline{64} \div \underline{8} = \underline{8}$

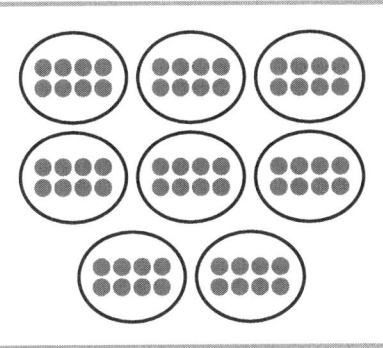

Array

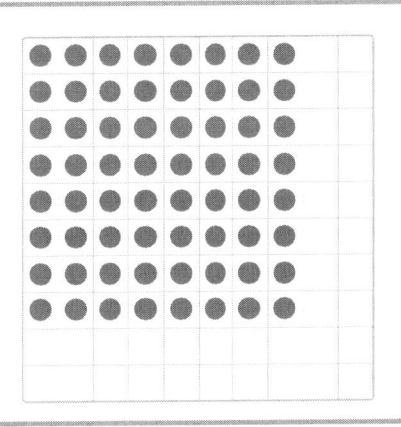

1. Word Problem
Morgan has 7 chickens. She collected 42 eggs from the chicken coop. If each chicken laid the same number of eggs, how many eggs did each chicken lay?

Picture

Equation
___ ÷ ___ = ___

Array

11.3 Solve Division Situations and Quantities

2. Word Problem

Julian rode 81 miles on his horse. He rode 9 miles each day. How many days did Julian ride his horse?

Picture

Equation

____ ÷ ____ = ____

Array

3. Word Problem

Jenny has 90 cows. She herded them into 10 equal groups. How many cows are in each group?

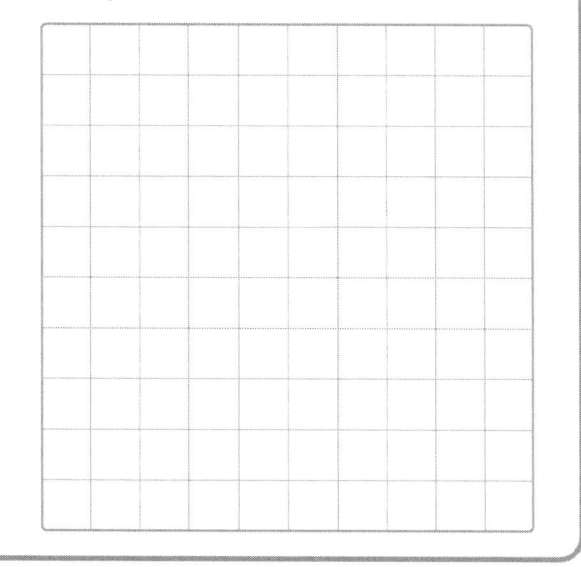

Picture

Equation

____ ÷ ____ = ____

Array

Name: _____ Date: _____

Related Facts

Read each division equation. Decide which operation will help you to find the unknown number. Then, write the related fact next to the equation.

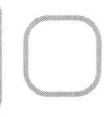

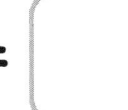

Division Equation	Related Fact
? ÷ 8 = 6	8 × 6 = ?
1. 42 ÷ ? = 7	☐ ☐ ☐ = ☐
2. ? ÷ 10 = 10	☐ ☐ ☐ = ☐
3. ? ÷ 9 = 8	☐ ☐ ☐ = ☐
4. 70 ÷ ? = 10	☐ ☐ ☐ = ☐
5. ? ÷ 9 = 7	☐ ☐ ☐ = ☐

11.4 Related Facts: Division and Multiplication

Name: _____ Date: _____

Let's Find Related Facts!

Find a related fact to help you solve for the unknown number. Use the strategy listed to find the unknown number. Do not forget to write down the unknown number!

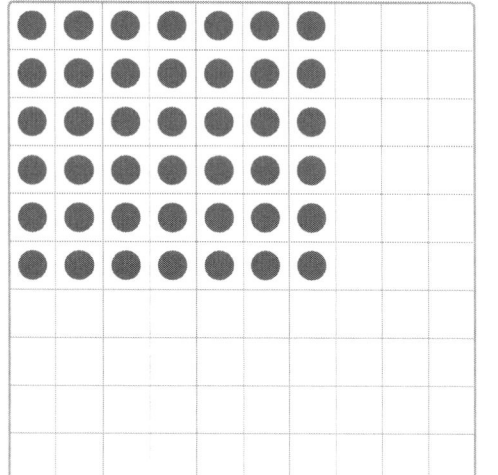

Example:

Division Equation

42 ÷ ? = 6

Related Fact

42 ÷ 6 = ?

Unknown Number

7

Array

1. **Division Equation**

? ÷ 9 = 7

Related Fact

_____

Unknown Number

_____

Multiplication Table

X	1	2	3	4	5	6	7	8	9	10
1	1	2	3	4	5	6	7	8	9	10
2	2	4	6	8	10	12	14	16	18	20
3	3	6	9	12	15	18	21	24	27	30
4	4	8	12	16	20	24	28	32	36	40
5	5	10	15	20	25	30	35	40	45	50
6	6	12	18	24	30	36	42	48	54	60
7	7	14	21	28	35	42	49	56	63	70
8	8	16	24	32	40	48	56	64	72	80
9	9	18	27	36	45	54	63	72	81	90
10	10	20	30	40	50	60	70	80	90	100

11.5 Division: Missing Numbers

Next page

2. Division Equation

$81 ÷ ? = 9$

Related Fact

_____

Unknown Number

_____

Repeated Subtraction

3. Division Equation

$? ÷ 8 = 10$

Related Fact

_____

Unknown Number

_____

Array

4. Division Equation

$? ÷ 7 = 8$

Related Fact

_____

Unknown Number

_____

Number Line

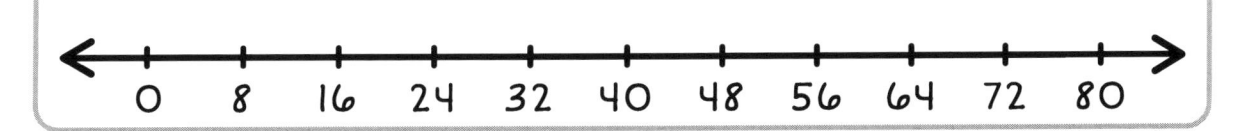

0 8 16 24 32 40 48 56 64 72 80

11.5 Division: Missing Numbers

5. Division Equation

$$72 \div \ ?\ = 8$$

Related Fact

_____

Unknown Number

_____

Division Picture

11.5 Division: Missing Numbers

Name: _____ Date: _____

Turkey Multiplication

Solve each equation. Then, match the answer to the color in the color key. Color each section.

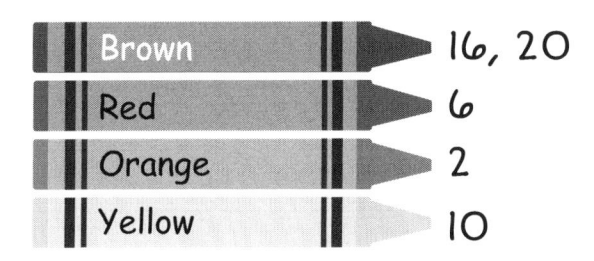

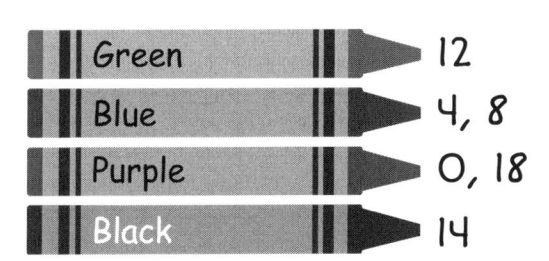

2 × 2 =
2 × 5 =
2 × 7 =
2 × 4 =
2 × 0 =
2 × 8 =
2 × 10 =
2 × 6 =
2 × 3 =
2 × 9 =
2 × 1 =

Brown	16, 20	Green	12
Red	6	Blue	4, 8
Orange	2	Purple	0, 18
Yellow	10	Black	14

12.1 Multiply by 2

Name: _____   Date: _____

Secret Message

Multiply each number. Then, find the blanks in the secret message below that match the product. Write the correct letter on each blank line to finish the sentence. Some letters may not be used.

1. 5 × 8 = ___ F	2. 5 × 5 = ___ T	3. 5 × 10 = ___ M
4. 5 × 6 = ___ V	5. 5 × 7 = ___ B	6. 10 × 9 = ___ D
7. 5 × 9 = ___ Y	8. 5 × 1 = ___ X	9. 5 × 2 = ___ S
10. 5 × 3 = ___ E	11. 5 × 4 = ___ A	12. 10 × 3 = ___ V
13. 10 × 5 = ___ M	14. 10 × 0 = ___ I	15. 5 × 0 = ___ I
16. 10 × 10 = ___ !	17. 10 × 1 = ___ S	18. 10 × 4 = ___ F
19. 10 × 8 = ___ H	20. 10 × 6 = ___ O	21. 10 × 7 = ___ R
	22. 10 × 2 = ___ A	

Thanksgiving...

__ __   __ __ __ __   __   __ __ __ __ __ __ __ __   __ __ __ __
0 10   20 30 20 10   40 20 30 60 70 0 25 15   25 0 50 15

__ __   __ __ __   __ __ __ __ __
60 40   25 80 15   45 15 20 70 100

131   12.2 Multiply by 10 and 5

Fall Feast

Solve each equation. Then, match each answer to the color. Color each section to reveal a colorful fall feast!

1. 1 x 8 = ☐ Blue
2. 1 x 6 = ☐ Brown
3. 1 x 1 = ☐ Red
4. 0 x 4 = ☐ Orange
5. 1 x 9 = ☐ Purple
6. 0 x 8 = ☐ Orange
7. 0 x 5 = ☐ Orange
8. 0 x 1 = ☐ Orange
9. 1 x 0 = ☐ Orange
10. 1 x 4 = ☐ Black
11. 1 x 10 = ☐ Green
12. 1 x 5 = ☐ Purple
13. 1 x 2 = ☐ Brown
14. 1 x 3 = ☐ Yellow
15. 1 x 7 = ☐ Red
16. 0 x 9 = ☐ Orange
17. 0 x 0 = ☐ Orange
18. 0 x 2 = ☐ Orange
19. 0 x 6 = ☐ Orange
20. 0 x 3 = ☐ Orange

12.3 Multiply by 1 and 0

HAPPY THANKSGIVING DAY

133

12.3 Multiply by 1 and 0

Multiplication Maze

Begin at Start to solve the multiplication problems. Follow the correct answer to the next problem to reach the End.

				start
3 x 5 — 15 — END — 12 — 3 x 2 — 30 — 3 x 10
3 / 0 / 15 / 9 / 6 / 20 / 10
3 x 0 — 1 — 3 x 1 — 30 — 3 x 7 — 21 — 3 x 6
24 / 45 / 20 / 7 / 9 / 18 / 25
3 x 8 — 13 — 3 x 9 — 12 — 3 x 4 — 4 — 3 x 1
21 / 27 / 40 / 4 / 15 / 0 / 10
3 x 7 — 6 — 3 x 2 — 5 — 3 x 3 — 3 — 3 x 8

12.4 Multiply by 3

134

Name: _____ Date: _____

Thanksgiving Multiplication

Read and solve each multiplication word problem. Remember to label your answer.

1. There are 2 groups of bread rolls. Each group has 10 bread rolls in it. How many bread rolls are there altogether?

   _____

2. Ava has 5 groups of 5 bowls. How many bowls does she have in all?

   _____

3. Ava counts 0 chairs for musical chairs. She has 3 players. How many chairs does she have?

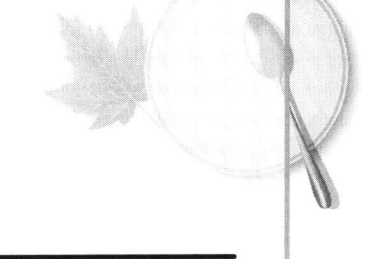

_____

4. Ava has 3 groups of 7 mini bags of chips. How many mini bags of chips does she have in all?

_____

5. Ava has 1 group of 8 board games. How many board games does she have in all?

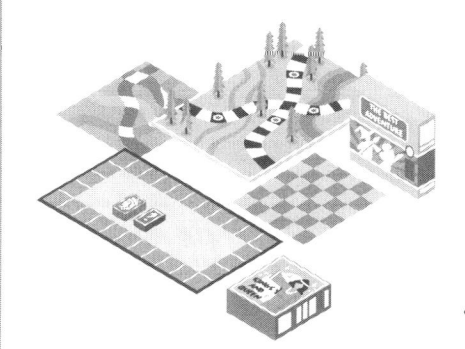

_____

12.5 Problem Solving: Reasoning with Multiplication Facts   136

Name: _____ Date: _____

Slime Monsters Take Over!

The slime monsters have changed the name of the lab! Find the product for each 6 fact. Match the answers below to the letter on each problem.

X	1	2	3	4	5	6	7	8	9	10
1	1	2	3	4	5	6	7	8	9	10
2	2	4	6	8	10	12	14	16	18	20
3	3	6	9	12	15	18	21	24	27	30
4	4	8	12	16	20	24	28	32	36	40
5	5	10	15	20	25	30	35	40	45	50
6	6	12	18	24	30	36	42	48	54	60
7	7	14	21	28	35	42	49	56	63	70
8	8	16	24	32	40	48	56	64	72	80
9	9	18	27	36	45	54	63	72	81	90
10	10	20	30	40	50	60	70	80	90	100

6 x 10 = 60
S

6 x 3 = ___
E

6 x 7 = ___
O

6 x 2 = ___
A

6 x 9 = ___
T

6 x 6 = ___
R

6 x 4 = ___
M

6 x 5 = ___
L

6 x 8 = ___
B

13.1 Multiply By 6
Next page

S _ I _
60 30 24 18

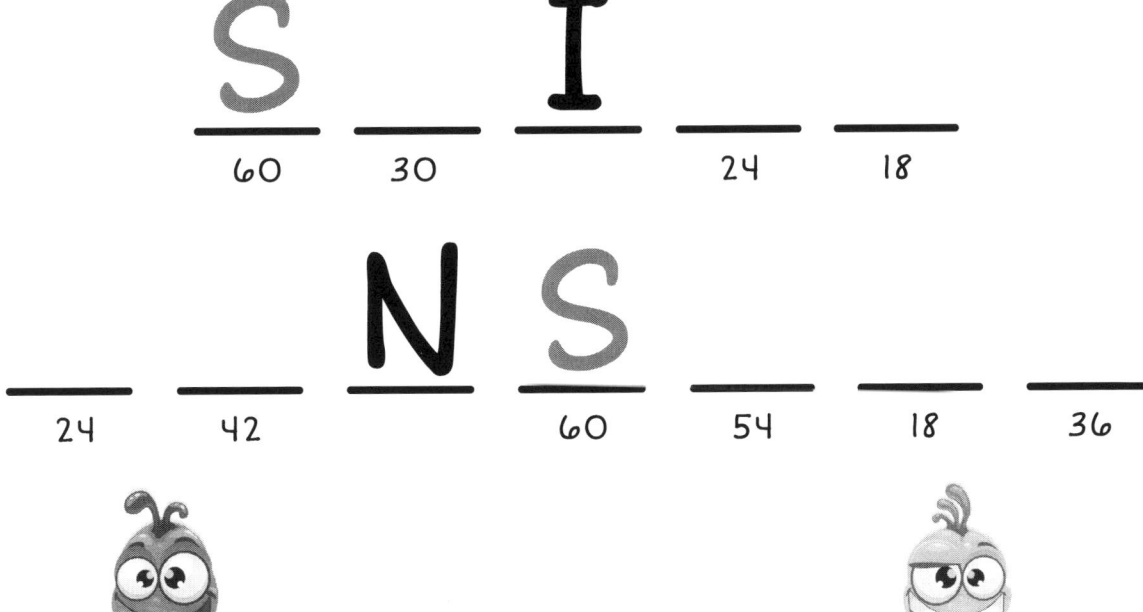

_ _ N S _ _
24 42   60 54 18 36

_ _ _
30 12 48

13.1 Multiply By 6

Name: _____ Date: _____

Making Rock Candy

Multiply each number. Then, match the answer to the letter in the secret message alphabet key. Write the letter on the blank below to finish the sentence.

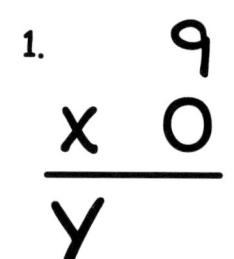

1. 9
   × 0
   ———
    Y

2. 9
   × 5
   ———
    P

3. 2
   × 9
   ———
    I

4. 7
   × 9
   ———
    H

5. 4
   × 9
   ———
    C

6. 8
   × 9
   ———
    A

7. 9
   × 6
   ———
    T

8. 9
   × 2
   ———
    K

9. 6
   × 9
   ———
    F

10. 9
    × 7
    ———
     Q

11. 9
    × 9
    ———
     R

12. 9
    × 8
    ———
     D

139

13.2 Multiply by 9

Next page

13. 5
    × 9
    ———
    X

14. 1
    × 9
    ———
    S

15. 9
    × 4
    ———
    C

16. 0
    × 9
    ———
    J

17. 9
    × 3
    ———
    M

18. 9
    × 9
    ———
    R

19. 10
    × 9
    ———
    E

20. 3
    × 9
    ———
    M

Making Rock Candy...

__ __
18   9

__ __ __ __ __ __ __ __ __ !
36 63 90 27 18 9 54 81 0

13.2 Multiply by 9

Name: _____   Date: _____

Volcano Multiplication

Multiply each number. Then, match the answer to the color in the color key. Color each section.

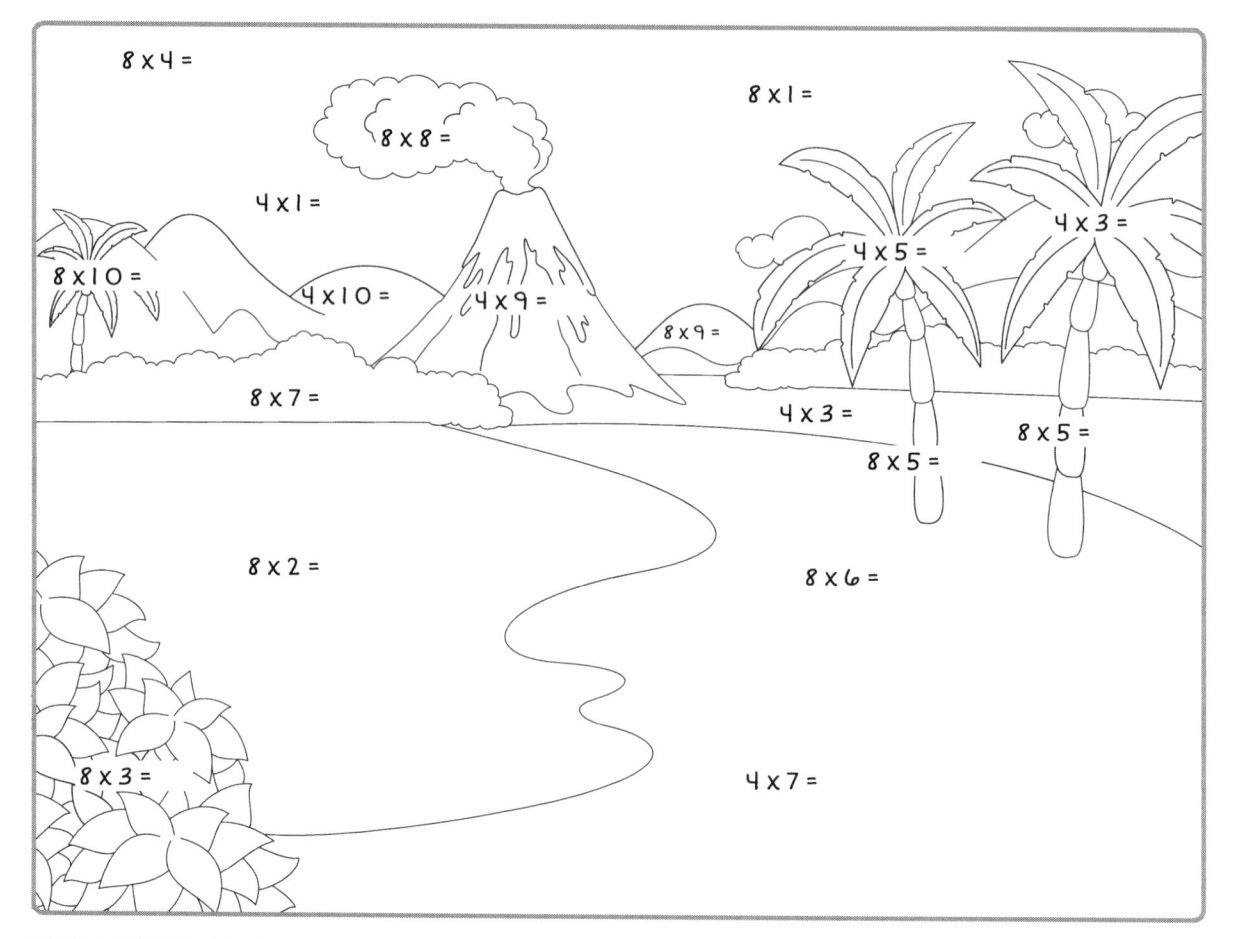

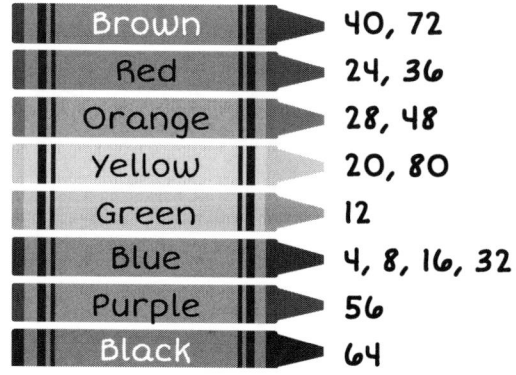

8 x 4 =
8 x 8 =
8 x 1 =
4 x 1 =
4 x 5 =
4 x 3 =
8 x 10 =
4 x 10 =
4 x 9 =
8 x 9 =
8 x 7 =
4 x 3 =
8 x 5 =
8 x 5 =
8 x 2 =
8 x 6 =
8 x 3 =
4 x 7 =

Brown	40, 72
Red	24, 36
Orange	28, 48
Yellow	20, 80
Green	12
Blue	4, 8, 16, 32
Purple	56
Black	64

141

13.3 Multiply By 4 and 8

Name: _____ Date: _____

Multiplication Wheel of 7

Fill in the multiplication wheel with the products. Look at the example of 7 x 1 = 7 in the wheel. Then choose four multiplication facts of 7 from the wheel and write them in the circles to form equations.

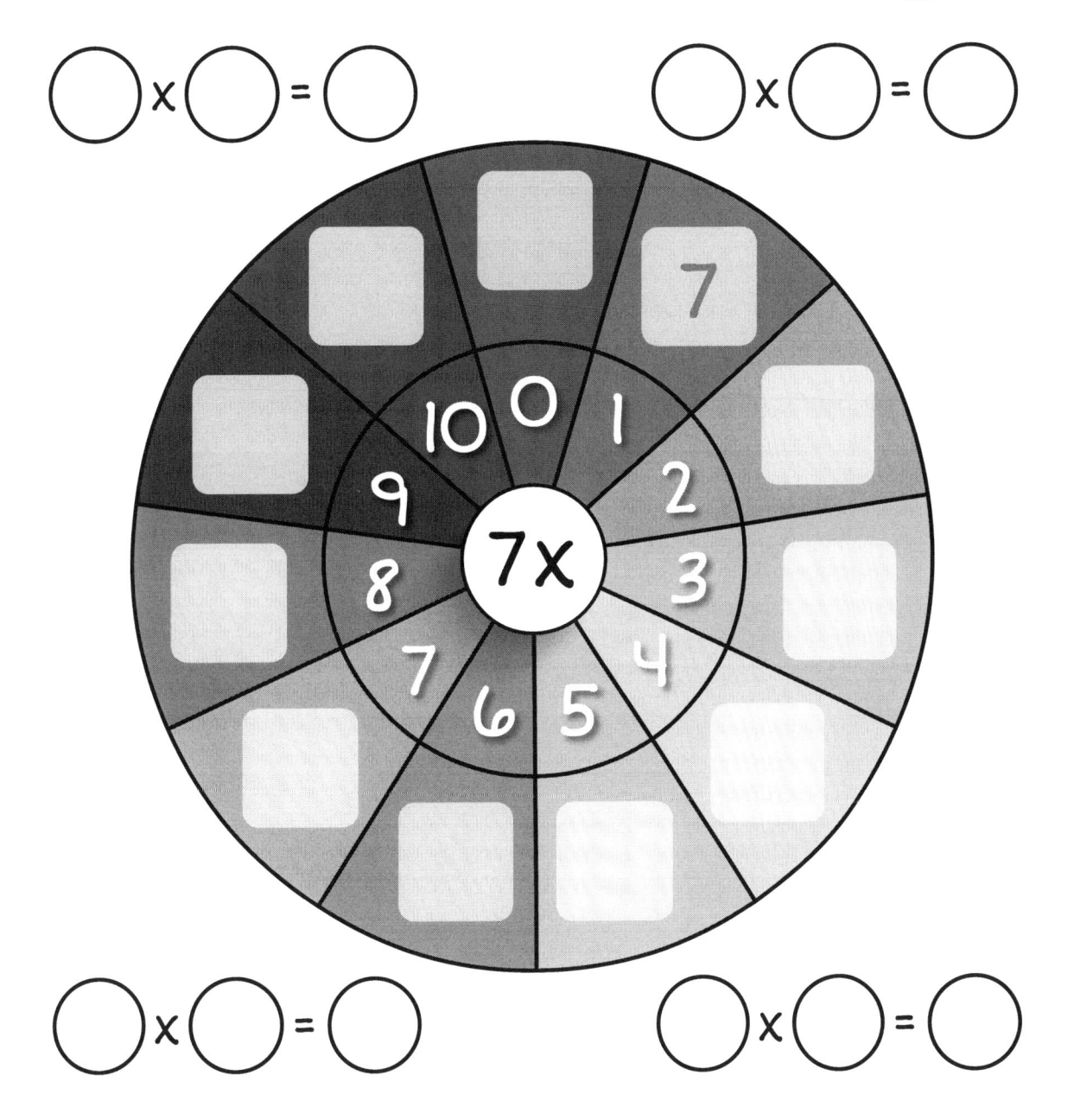

◯ x ◯ = ◯   ◯ x ◯ = ◯

◯ x ◯ = ◯   ◯ x ◯ = ◯

13.4 Multiply by 7   142

Name: _____ Date: _____

New House Party Multiplication

Read and solve each multiplication word problem.

Daniel is having a new house party! He is preparing the food and games.

1. Daniel starts with hamburger sliders. He has 7 friends coming over and makes 3 sliders for each. How many sliders does he make?

   _____

2. Daniel also makes fresh lemonade. He uses 2 lemons per glass. He makes 6 glasses of lemonade. How many lemons did he use?

   _____

3. Next, he starts preparing the 5 games. Each game takes 8 minutes to prepare. How much time does it take for Daniel to prepare all 5 games?

   _____

13.5 Problem Solving: Reasoning with Multiplication Facts

Next page

4. 9 of Daniel's friends decide to bring muffins. Each friend brings 6 muffins. How many muffins do they bring in total?

_____

5. Daniel is planning his expenses for the party. He has 5 games planned and wants to spend $4 per game. How much money does he need for all the games?

_____

13.5 Problem Solving: Reasoning with Multiplication Facts

Name: _____ Date: _____

Divide By 1
Find the quotients for the equations below.

Divide by 1 Rule:

Find the quotients below using the Divide by 1 Rule. Then, use each quotient to color the picture.

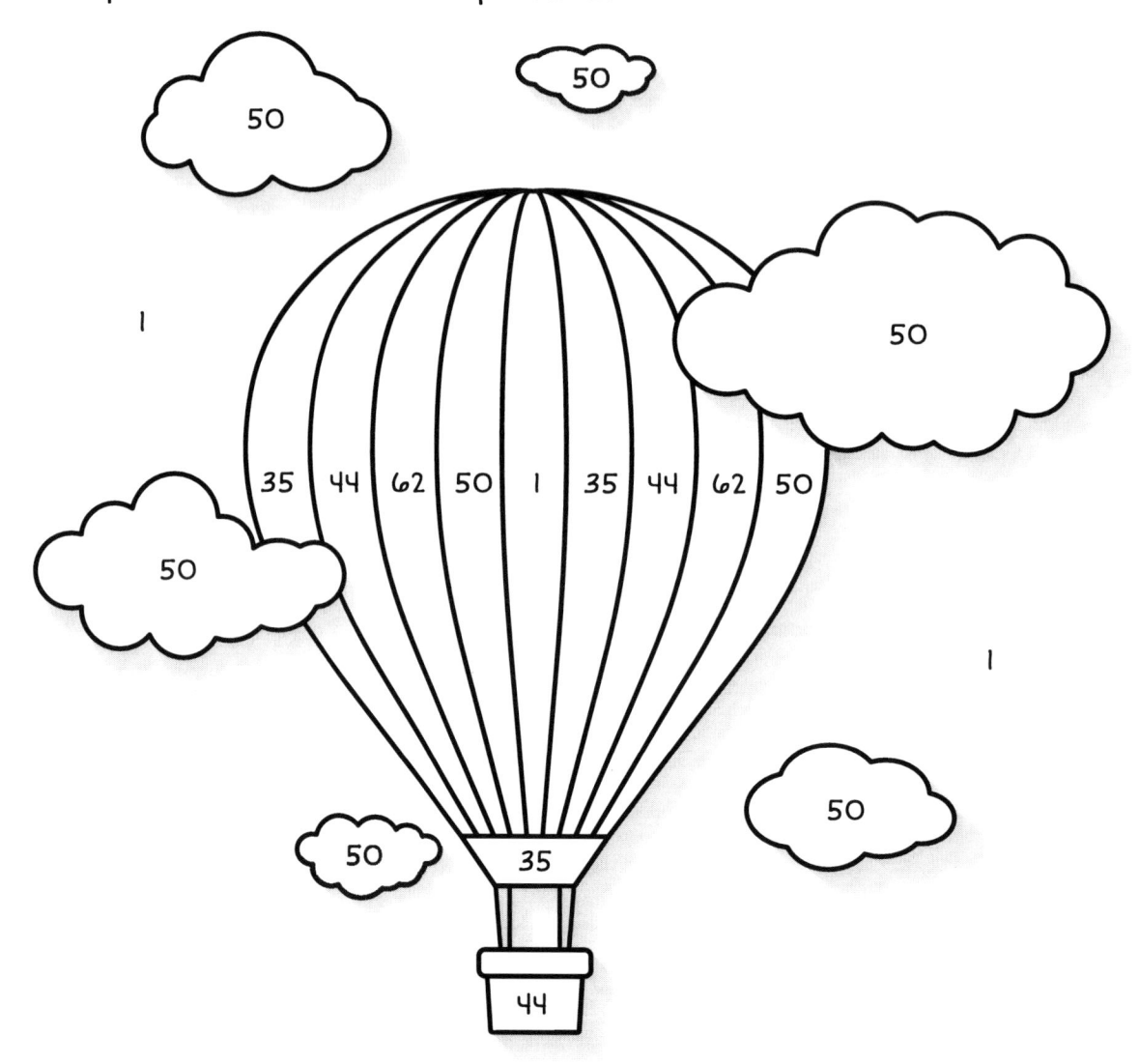

Red	Purple	Blue	Yellow	Green
$35 \div 1 = ?$	$50 \div 1 = ?$	$28 \div 28 = ?$	$44 \div 1 = ?$	$62 \div 1 = ?$

Find the quotients using the strategies indicated.

Example: Find this quotient by drawing an array.

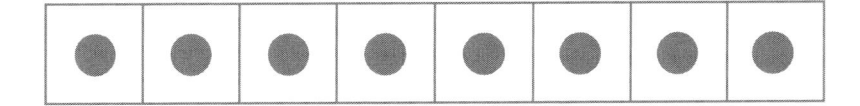

$$8 \div 1 = \boxed{8}$$

Find this quotient by drawing an array.

$$5 \div 1 = \boxed{}$$

Example: Find this quotient using repeated subtraction.

$$12 \div 12 = \boxed{1}$$

$$12-1-1-1-1-1-1-1-1-1-1-1-1=0$$

Find this quotient using repeated subtraction.

$$6 \div 1 = \boxed{}$$

14.1 Divide By 1

Name: _____ Date: _____

Divide by 2 and 3

Can you find the missing quotients using a division strategy?

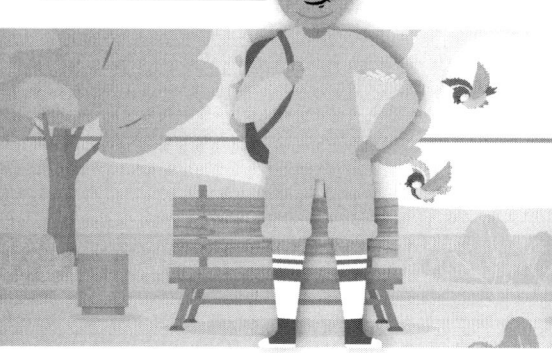

Can you find the missing quotients using a division strategy? Use the listed strategies below and write your answer in the blank. Do not forget to show your work!

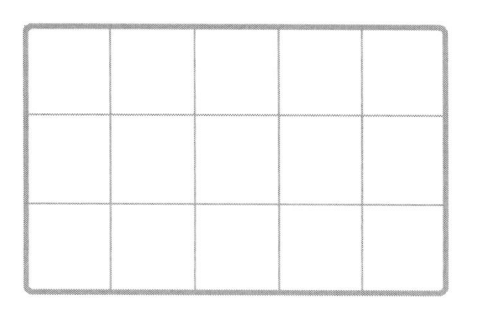

Array

15 ÷ 3 = ☐

Pictures

4 ÷ 2 = ☐

Repeated Subtraction

14 ÷ 2 = ☐

Multiplication Table

6 ÷ 3 = ☐

x	1	2	3	4	5	6	7	8	9	10
1	1	2	3	4	5	6	7	8	9	10
2	2	4	6	8	10	12	14	16	18	20
3	3	6	9	12	15	18	21	24	27	30
4	4	8	12	16	20	24	28	32	36	40
5	5	10	15	20	25	30	35	40	45	50
6	6	12	18	24	30	36	42	48	54	60
7	7	14	21	28	35	42	49	56	63	70
8	8	16	24	32	40	48	56	64	72	80
9	9	18	27	36	45	54	63	72	81	90
10	10	20	30	40	50	60	70	80	90	100

What multiplication facts help you find these missing quotients? Write each multiplication sentence below and record the missing quotient.

18 ÷ 3 = ☐
___ X ___ = ___

24 ÷ 3 = ☐
___ X ___ = ___

16 ÷ 2 = ☐
___ X ___ = ___

12 ÷ 2 = ☐
___ X ___ = ___

Use the numbers given to write related division and multiplication facts.

	Division	Multiplication
20, 2, 10		
27, 9, 3		
12, 3, 4		
10, 2, 5		

14.2 Divide By 2 and 3

Name: _____ Date: _____

Divide by 4 and 5

Division facts and multiplication facts are related. On this worksheet, you will use multiplication facts to solve division sentences. Write the missing numbers in the blanks below to complete each equation.

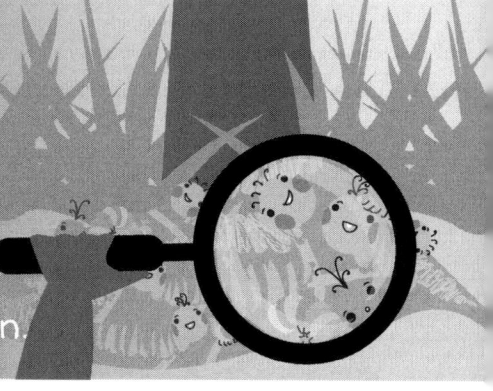

5 x __7__ = 35   and   35 ÷ 5 = ____

4 x ____ = 8   and   8 ÷ 4 = ____

5 x ____ = 30   and   30 ÷ 5 = ____

5 x ____ = 45   and   45 ÷ 5 = ____

4 x ____ = 36   and   36 ÷ 4 = ____

4 x ____ = 16   and   16 ÷ 4 = ____

5 x ____ = 5   and   5 ÷ 5 = ____

5 x ____ = 20   and   20 ÷ 5 = ____

4 x ____ = 32   and   32 ÷ 4 = ____

5 x ____ = 10   and   10 ÷ 5 = ____

4 x ____ = 40   and   40 ÷ 4 = ____

Name: _____ Date: _____

Solve Word Problems
Can you solve division word problems?

Read each word problem. Find the quotient by writing the division fact in the blanks.

Ava planted 14 seeds equally in 2 rows. How many seeds did she plant in each row?

___ ÷ ___ = ___

Caleb brought 5 bouncy balls to school. He gave them to 5 of his friends. How many bouncy balls did each friend get?

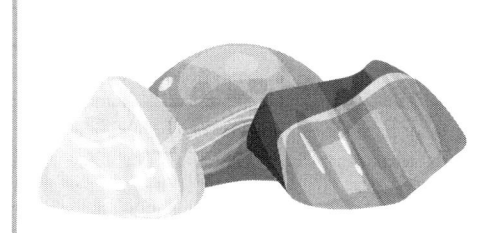

___ ÷ ___ = ___

Madelyn shared 30 polished rocks equally among 5 friends. How many rocks did each friend get?

___ ÷ ___ = ___

14.5 Problem Solving: Reasoning with Division Facts

A squirrel gathered 28 nuts and hid them equally in 4 different logs. How many nuts are in each log?

____ ÷ ____ = ____

A zookeeper has 12 bananas. The bananas are divided equally among 3 monkeys. How many bananas does each monkey get?

____ ÷ ____ = ____

Solve these word problems using related multiplication facts.

A rope is 4 meters long. If Daniel cuts it into 2 equal lengths, how long are the rope pieces?

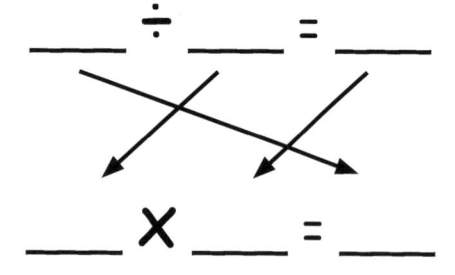

____ ÷ ____ = ____

____ × ____ = ____

____ meters

Zoe hiked 24 miles in 3 days. How many miles did she hike each day?

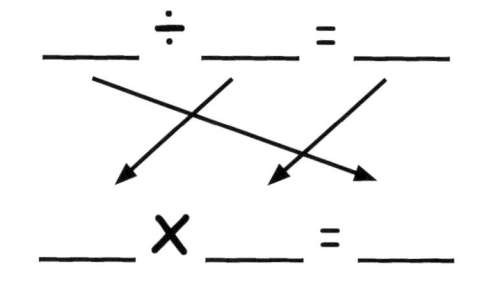

____ ÷ ____ = ____

____ × ____ = ____

____ miles

Name: _____ Date: _____

Divide by 6 and 7

Look at each picture. Write a multiplication and division sentence to represent the array.

Example:

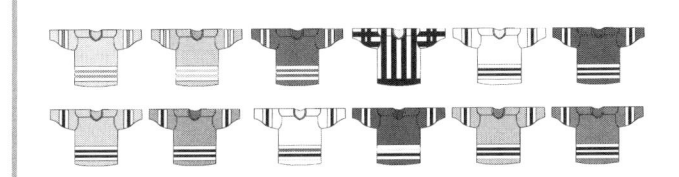

Multiplication Sentence:

<u>6</u> X <u>2</u> = <u>12</u>

Division Sentence:

<u>12</u> ÷ <u>6</u> = <u>2</u>

1.

Multiplication Sentence:

___ X ___ = ___

Division Sentence:

___ ÷ ___ = ___

2.

Multiplication Sentence:

___ X ___ = ___

Division Sentence:

___ ÷ ___ = ___

15.1 Divide by 6 and 7

152

Next page

3.

Multiplication Sentence:

___ X ___ = ___

Division Sentence:

___ ÷ ___ = ___

4.

Multiplication Sentence:

___ X ___ = ___

Division Sentence:

___ ÷ ___ = ___

5.

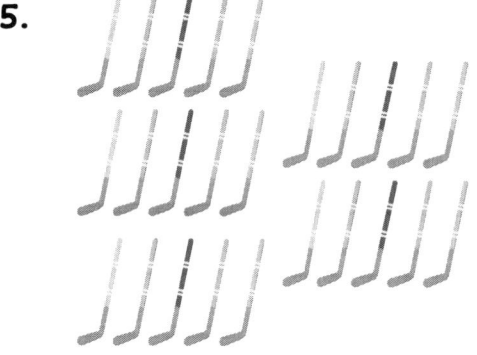

Multiplication Sentence:

___ X ___ = ___

Division Sentence:

___ ÷ ___ = ___

6.

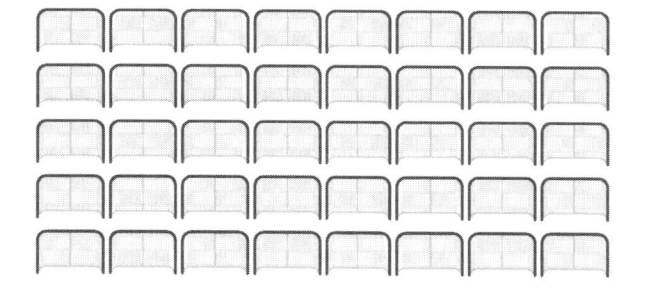

Multiplication Sentence:

___ X ___ = ___

Division Sentence:

___ ÷ ___ = ___

Name: _____ Date: _____

Divide by 8

Look at each picture. Write a multiplication and division sentence to represent the array.

Example:

Multiplication Sentence:

__8__ X __2__ = __16__

Division Sentence:

__16__ ÷ __8__ = __2__

1.

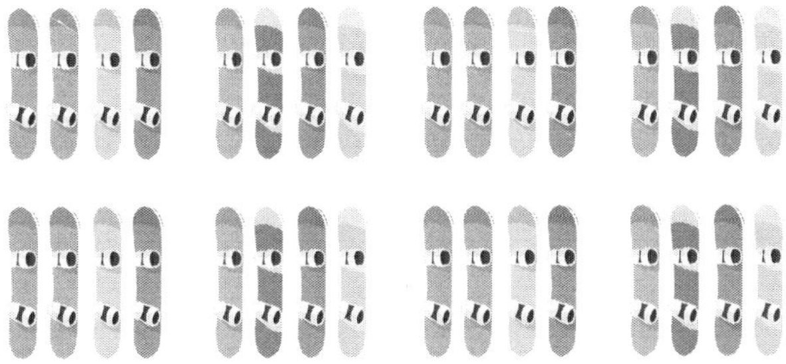

Multiplication Sentence:

___ X ___ = ___

Division Sentence:

___ ÷ ___ = ___

2.

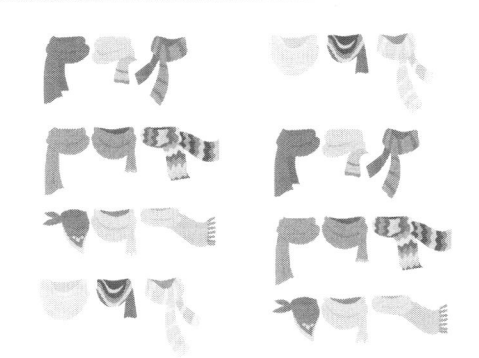

Multiplication Sentence:

___ X ___ = ___

Division Sentence:

___ ÷ ___ = ___

15.2 Divide by 8

3.

Multiplication Sentence:

___ X ___ = ___

Division Sentence:

___ ÷ ___ = ___

4.

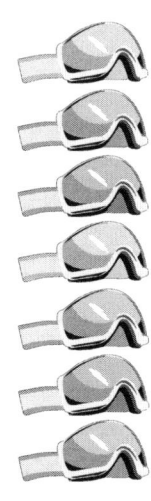

Multiplication Sentence:

___ X ___ = ___

Division Sentence:

___ ÷ ___ = ___

5.

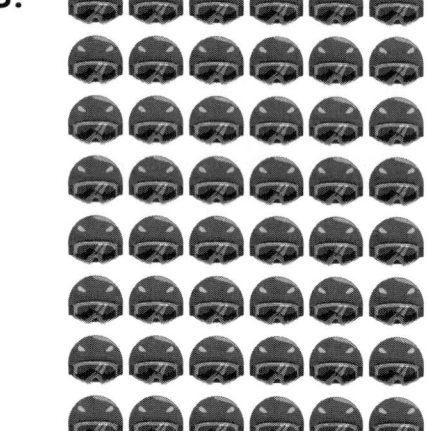

Multiplication Sentence:

___ X ___ = ___

Division Sentence:

___ ÷ ___ = ___

6.

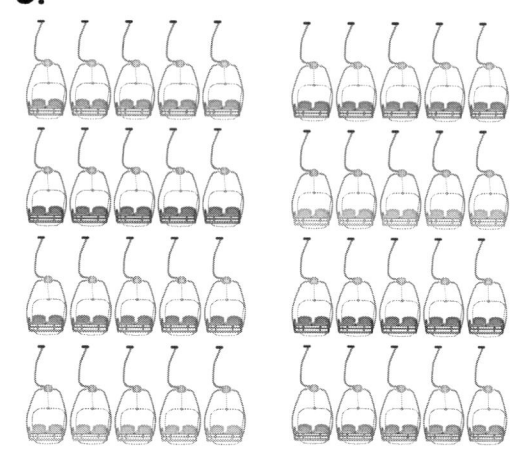

Multiplication Sentence:

___ X ___ = ___

Division Sentence:

___ ÷ ___ = ___

Name: _____ Date: _____

Divide by 9
Identify how multiplication and division relate using equal groups.

Look at the picture. Write both a multiplication sentence and a division sentence to represent the array.

Example:

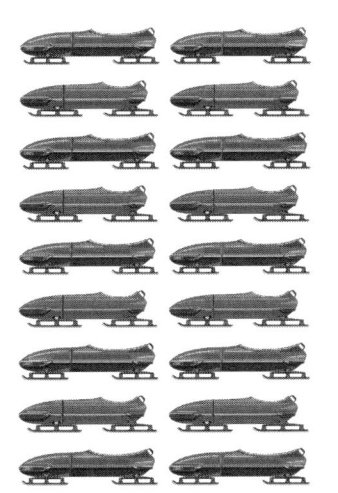

Multiplication Sentence:

$\underline{9} \times \underline{2} = \underline{18}$

Division Sentence:

$\underline{18} \div \underline{9} = \underline{2}$

1.

Multiplication Sentence:

___ × ___ = ___

Division Sentence:

___ ÷ ___ = ___

15.3 Divide by 9

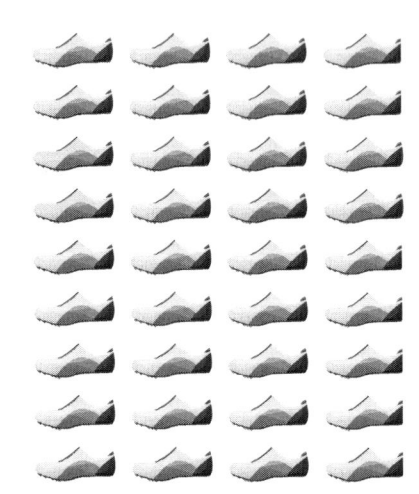

2.

Multiplication Sentence:

___ X ___ = ___

Division Sentence:

___ ÷ ___ = ___

3.

Multiplication Sentence:

___ X ___ = ___

Division Sentence:

___ ÷ ___ = ___

4.

Multiplication Sentence:

___ X ___ = ___

Division Sentence:

___ ÷ ___ = ___

Name: _____ Date: _____

A Skating Riddle

Solve each division equation. Use the quotients and the letters on the skates to solve the riddle.

I
70 ÷ 10 =

C
40 ÷ 10 =

R
20 ÷ 10 =

A
10 ÷ 10 =

E
50 ÷ 10 =

P
80 ÷ 10 =

H
90 ÷ 10 =

U
60 ÷ 10 =

G
100 ÷ 10 =

K
30 ÷ 10 =

T __ __ __ __ __   M __ __ T __ __ __ __ __ __ __ !
 9 5 7 4 5   7 10 9   4 2 1 4 3 6 8

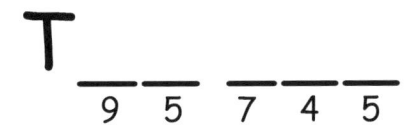

15.4 Divide by 10   158

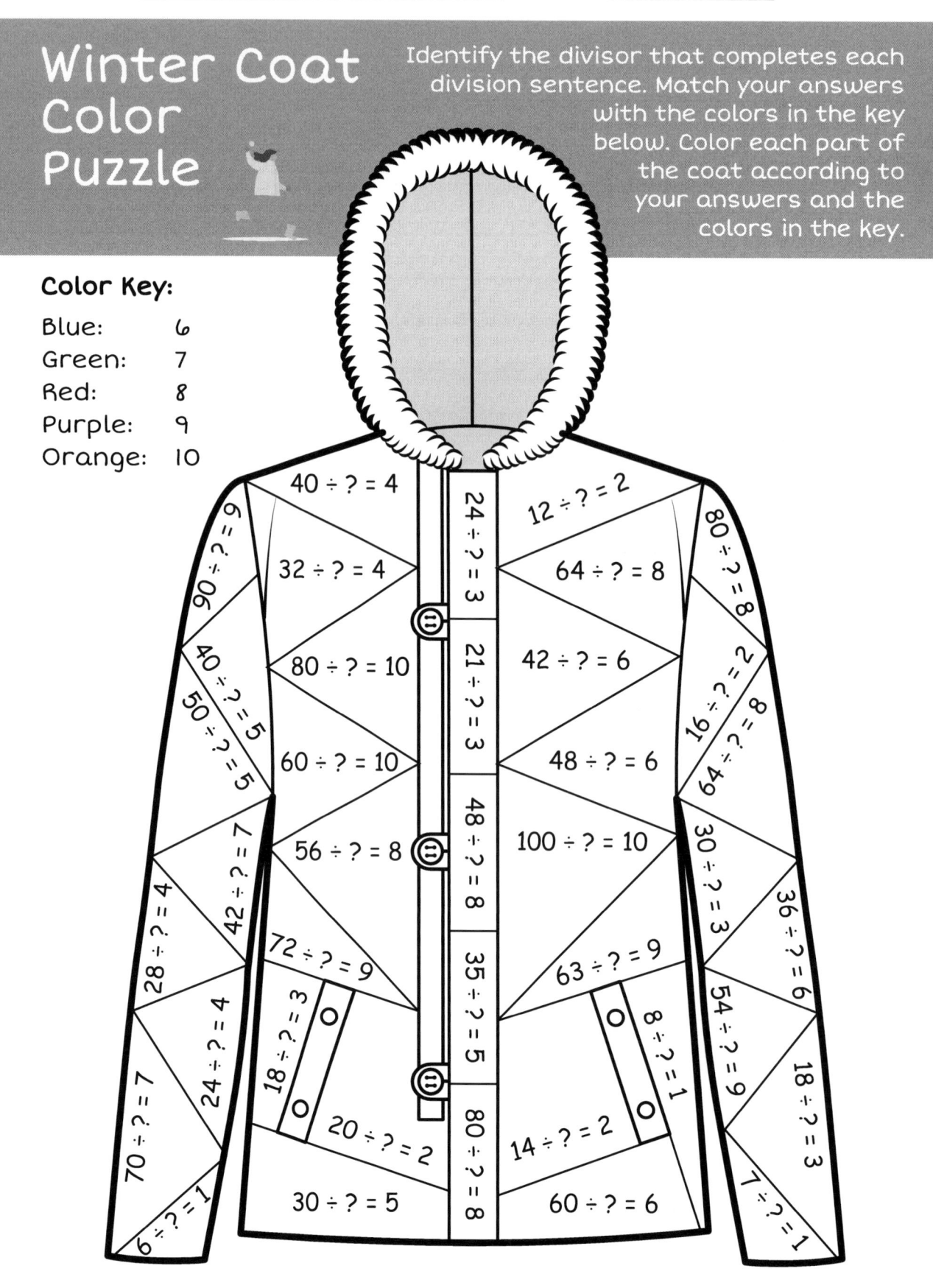

Name: _____ Date: _____

Winter Coat Color Puzzle

Identify the divisor that completes each division sentence. Match your answers with the colors in the key below. Color each part of the coat according to your answers and the colors in the key.

Color Key:

Blue: 6
Green: 7
Red: 8
Purple: 9
Orange: 10

40 ÷ ? = 4
90 ÷ ? = 9
32 ÷ ? = 4
24 ÷ ? = 3
12 ÷ ? = 2
64 ÷ ? = 8
80 ÷ ? = 8
40 ÷ ? = 5
80 ÷ ? = 10
21 ÷ ? = 3
42 ÷ ? = 6
16 ÷ ? = 2
50 ÷ ? = 5
60 ÷ ? = 10
48 ÷ ? = 6
64 ÷ ? = 8
42 ÷ ? = 7
56 ÷ ? = 8
48 ÷ ? = 8
100 ÷ ? = 10
30 ÷ ? = 3
28 ÷ ? = 4
72 ÷ ? = 9
35 ÷ ? = 5
63 ÷ ? = 9
36 ÷ ? = 6
24 ÷ ? = 4
18 ÷ ? = 3
8 ÷ ? = 1
54 ÷ ? = 9
18 ÷ ? = 3
70 ÷ ? = 7
20 ÷ ? = 2
80 ÷ ? = 8
14 ÷ ? = 2
60 ÷ ? = 6
6 ÷ ? = 1
30 ÷ ? = 5
7 ÷ ? = 1

159

15.5 Divide by 6 Through 10

Name: _____ Date: _____

Non-Unit Fractions

Complete the table by writing the name of each non-unit fraction. Then shade each shape to show the fraction for the row.

Fraction	Partitioned Shape	Written Fraction
$\dfrac{7}{8}$	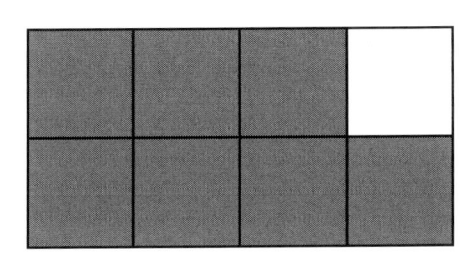	seven eighths
——	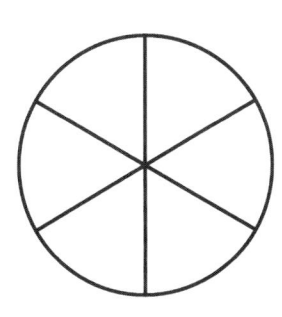	three sixths
$\dfrac{3}{4}$	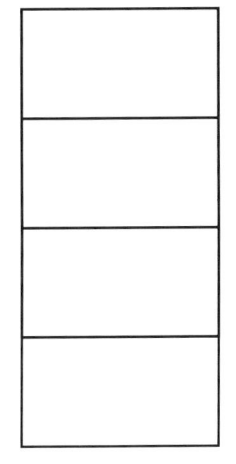	

16.2 Non-Unit Fractions

Fraction	Partitioned Shape	Written Fraction
—	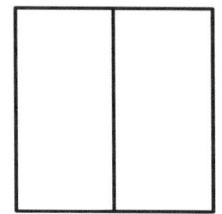	two halves and/or one whole
$\frac{4}{6}$	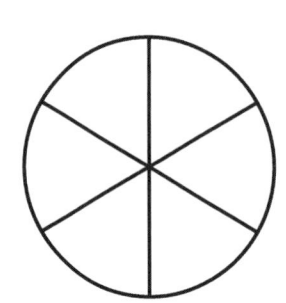	
—	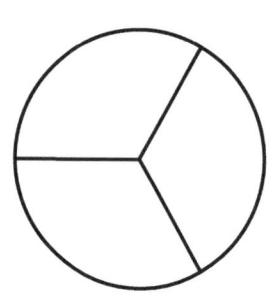	two thirds

16.2 Non-Unit Fractions

Name: _____   Date: _____

Find the Numerators and Denominators!

Use what you know about fractions to answer the questions.

1.

What is the denominator of this partitioned shape? _____

What is the numerator of this partitioned shape? _____

What fraction of this shape is yellow? _____

What fraction of this shape is white? _____

2. Partition each of these shapes to match the denominators below.

Denominator: 6
sixths

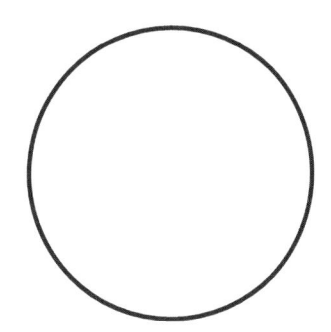

Denominator: 4
fourths

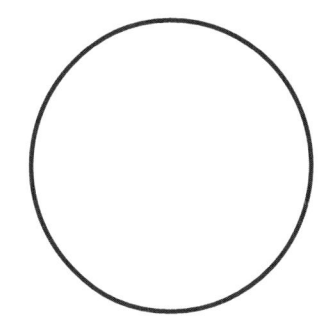

Denominator: 3
thirds

Helpful hint: Start drawing your lines from the middle of the circle.

16.3 Numerator and Denominator

3. Color each of these partitioned shapes to match the numerators below. Then write the fraction of the shaded parts.

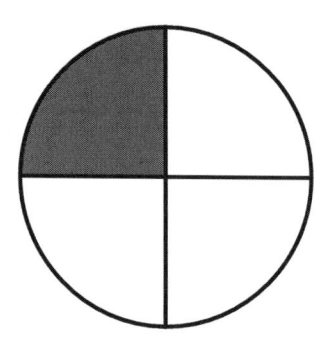

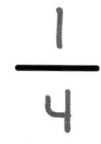

Numerator: 1   Numerator: 5 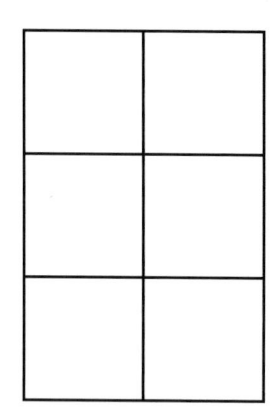   Numerator: 6

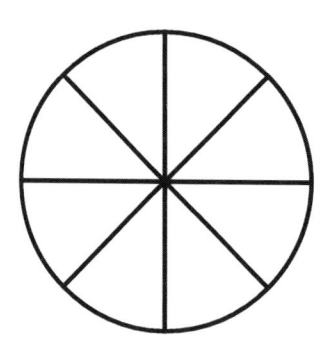

$$\frac{1}{4}$$

Name: _____ Date: _____

Create Fractions

Use what you know about fractions to answer the questions.

1. Color these shapes to create the fractions below.

$$\frac{2}{4}$$ $$\frac{4}{6}$$ 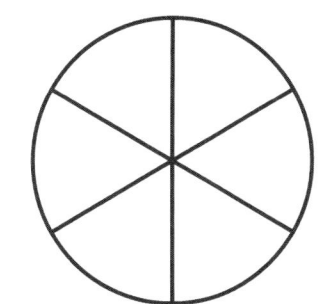 $$\frac{3}{8}$$

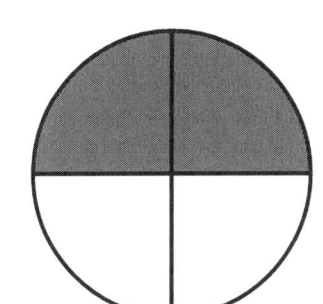

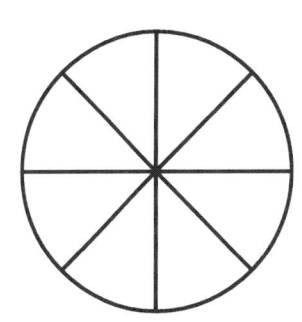

$$\frac{6}{6}$$ 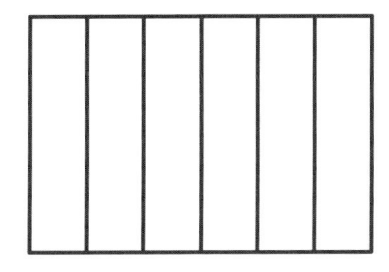 $$\frac{1}{3}$$ 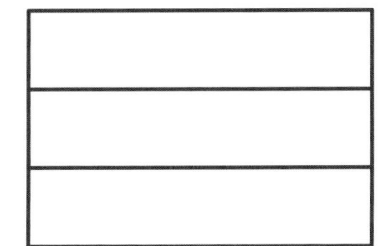 $$\frac{5}{8}$$

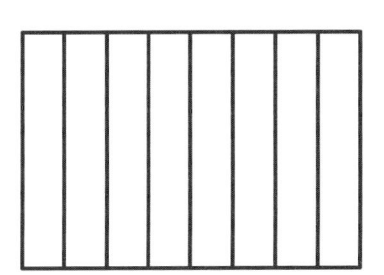

16.4 Fractions of a Whole

2. Partition and color these shapes to create the fractions below.

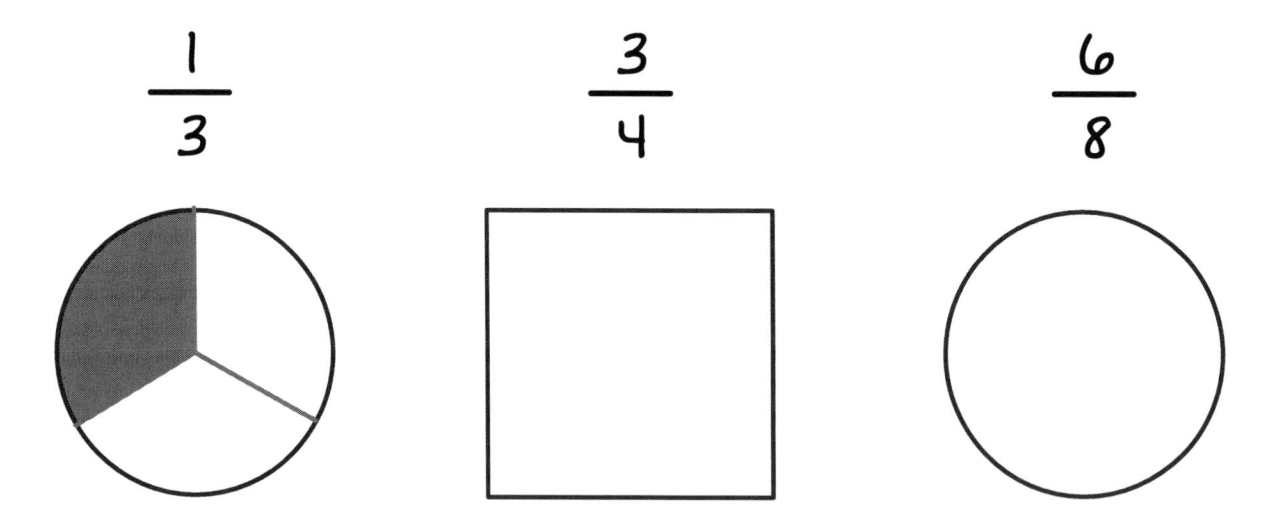

$\frac{1}{3}$　　　　　　$\frac{3}{4}$　　　　　　$\frac{6}{8}$

3. Think about this!
   How do you know this fraction shows $\frac{5}{8}$?

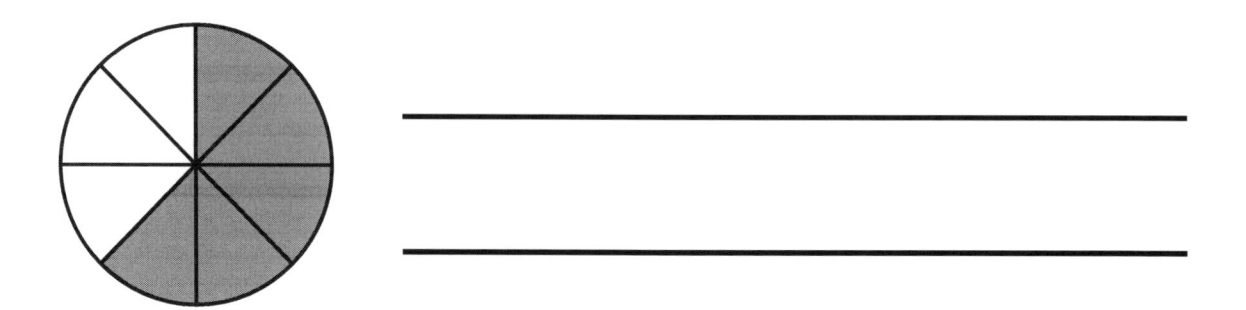

   _____

   _____

165　　　　　　　　　　　　　　　　　　16.4 Fractions of a Whole

Name: _____   Date: _____

Candy Fractions

Place one candy in each circle below. Then answer each question about fractions on the right. (If you do not have colorful candies, you can color the circles according to the color labels.)

Candies | Fractions

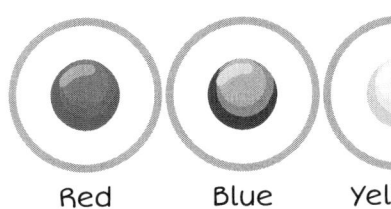

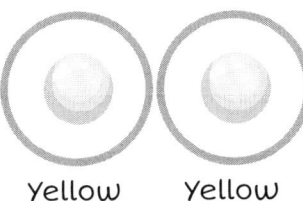

Red Blue Yellow Yellow

What fraction of the candies are red?

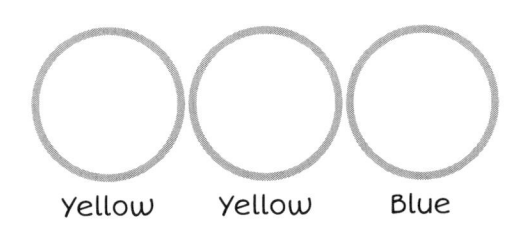

$$\frac{1}{4}$$

What fraction of the candies are yellow?

$$\frac{2}{4}$$

Yellow Yellow Blue

What fraction of the candies are yellow?

What fraction of the candies are blue?

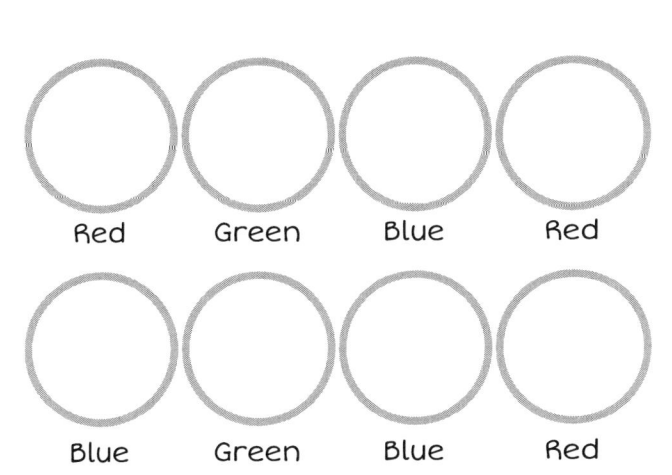

Red Green Blue Red
Blue Green Blue Red

What fraction of the candies are blue?

What fraction of the candies are green?

16.5 Fractions of a Group

166
Next page

Candies

○ ○ ○ ○
Green Green Green Red

Fractions

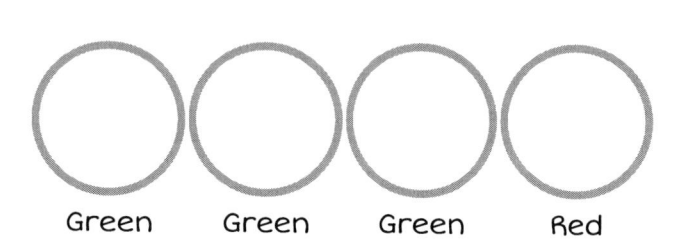

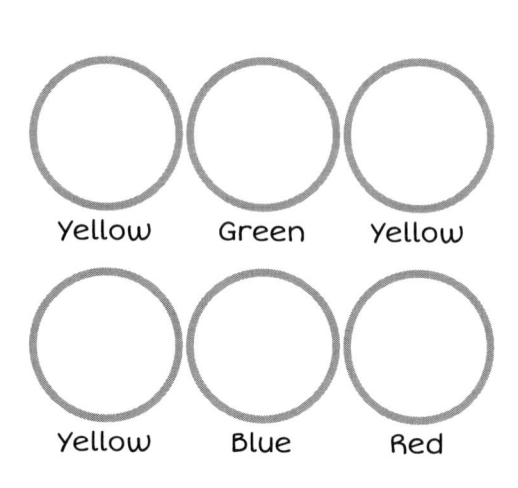

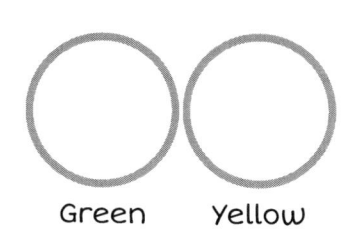

What fraction of the candies are red?

What fraction of the candies are green?

○ ○ ○
Yellow Green Yellow

○ ○ ○
Yellow Blue Red

What fraction of the candies are yellow?

What fraction of the candies are red?

○ ○
Green Yellow

What fraction of the candies are yellow?

What fraction of the candies are green?

16.5 Fractions of a Group

Name: _____ Date: _____

Can You Show the Fractions?
Color in the partitioned rectangles.
Then draw a dot to mark each fraction.

1. $\dfrac{2}{4}$

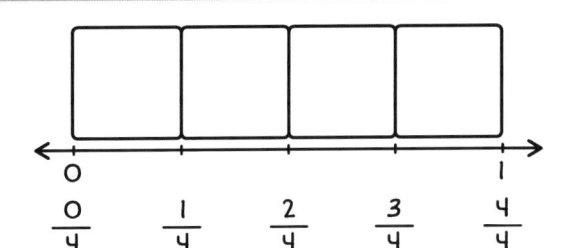

2. $\dfrac{4}{4}$

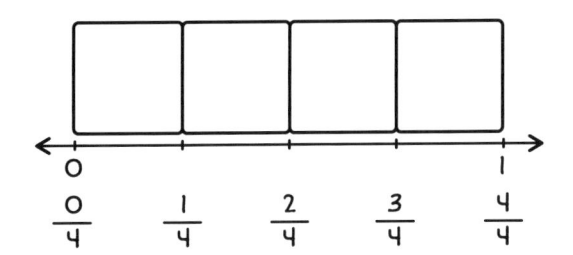

3. $\dfrac{0}{4}$

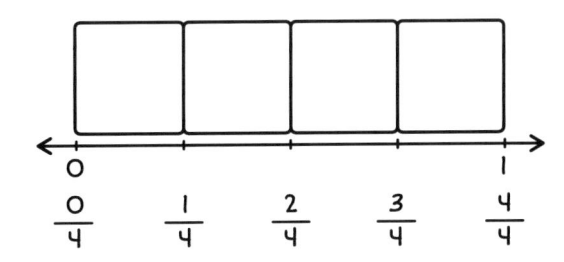

4. $\dfrac{3}{4}$

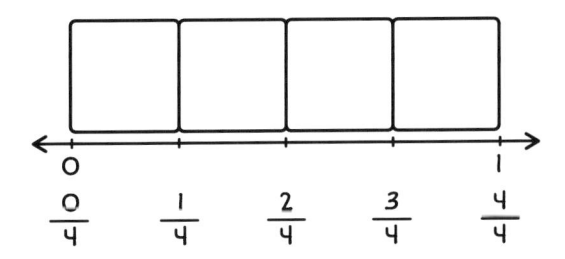

5. $\dfrac{1}{4}$

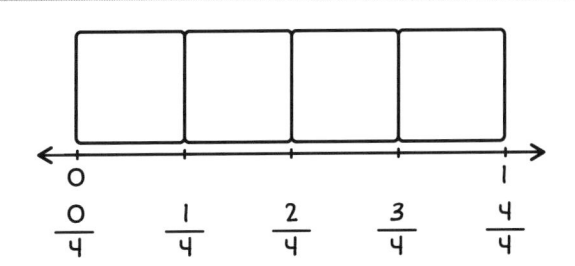

17.1 0 to 1 on a Number Line

Name: _____ Date: _____

Partition Wholes!

Follow the steps below to make a partitioned whole on a number line.
1. Partition and color the rectangle to match the fraction.
2. Draw line segments on the number line, and label each fraction.
3. Place a dot above the correct fraction on the number line.

Example:

$\dfrac{2}{3}$

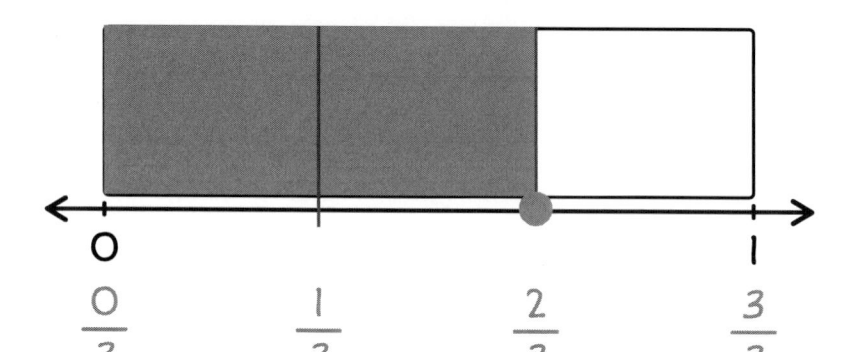

$\dfrac{0}{3}$ $\dfrac{1}{3}$ $\dfrac{2}{3}$ $\dfrac{3}{3}$

1.

$\dfrac{2}{2}$

2.

$\dfrac{5}{6}$

169

17.2 Equal Parts

Next page

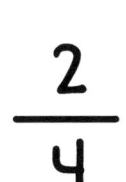

3.

$\dfrac{2}{4}$

4.

$\dfrac{3}{8}$

17.2 Equal Parts

Name: _____ Date: _____

Identify the Fractions

Write the numerator and denominator for the fraction shown on each number line.

Fraction	Number Line

Example:

$\dfrac{2}{3}$

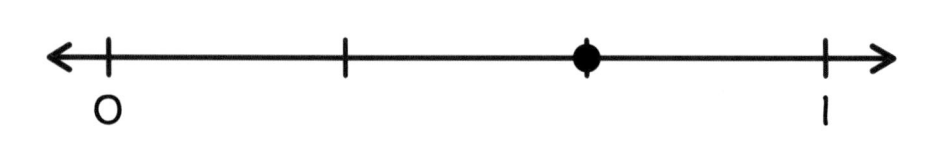

0 •———————————• 1 (dot at 2/3)

1.

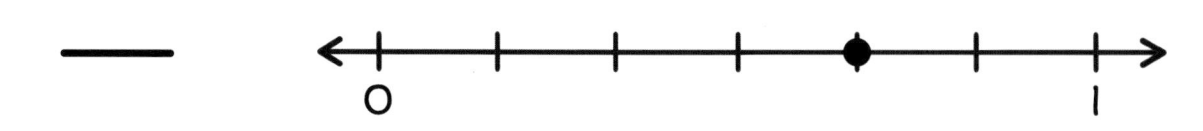

___ 0 •———•———•———•———•———• 1 (dot at 4/6)

2.

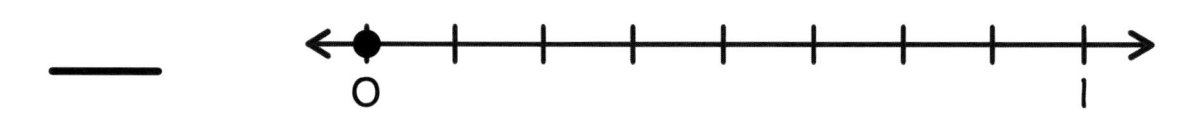

___ 0 •———————————————• 1 (dot at 0/8)

3.

___ 0 •———————• 1 (dot at 1/4)

171   17.3 Fractions on a Number Line

4.

_____ number line with 0 to 1 divided into 4 parts, dot on 3rd tick (3/4)

5.

_____ number line with 0 to 1, dot in the middle (1/2)

6. **Challenge Question:** Draw a number line and record the fraction $\frac{2}{2}$.

17.3 Fractions on a Number Line

Name: _____ Date: _____

Create and Record Fractions on a Number Line

Read each word problem. Record the correct fractions on the number lines.

Example:

Caleb's pizza was cut into 8 slices. He ate 2 slices. What fraction of the pizza did Caleb eat? Record it on the number line below.

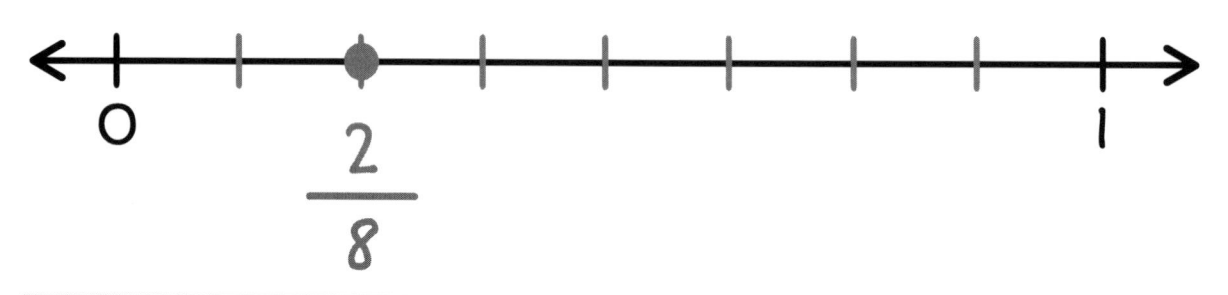

$$\frac{2}{8}$$

1. Ava's hat is made up of 4 red squares and 2 orange squares. What fraction of Ava's hat is red? Record it on the number line below.

2. Madelyn is making an blocks of snow. She has made 4 blocks of snow. 3 of the blocks have leaves in them. What fraction of the snow blocks have leaves? Record it on the number line below.

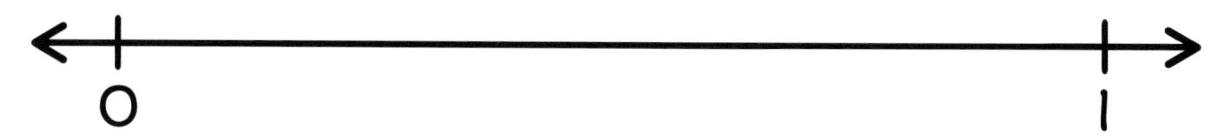

173

17.5 Word Problems with Fractions

3. An ice-skating rink is divided into 3 sections. Logan has skated in 2 of the sections. What fraction of the ice-skating rink has Logan skated in? Record it on the number line below.

←|—————————————————————————|→
 0   1

4. A ski lift has 8 chairs. Daniel and his friends are sitting on 4 of the chairs. What fraction of the ski lift are they sitting on? Record it on the number line below.

←|—————————————————————————|→
 0   1

5. Zoe drank half a mug of hot cocoa. What fraction of the hot cocoa did she drink? Record it on the number line below.

←|—————————————————————————|→
 0   1

17.5 Word Problems with Fractions

Name: _____ Date: _____

Color Equivalent Fractions

Create equivalent fractions by coloring each blank partitioned shape to match each shaded shape below. Then write the fraction under each shape you colored.

Example:

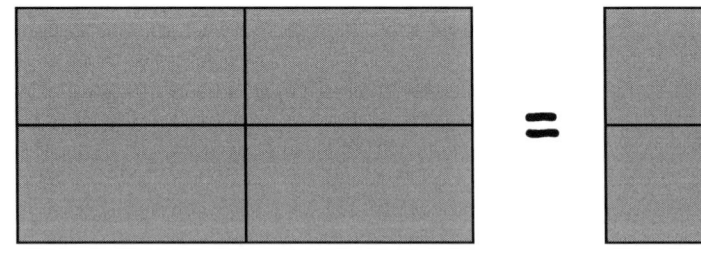

$$\frac{4}{4} = \frac{6}{6}$$

1.

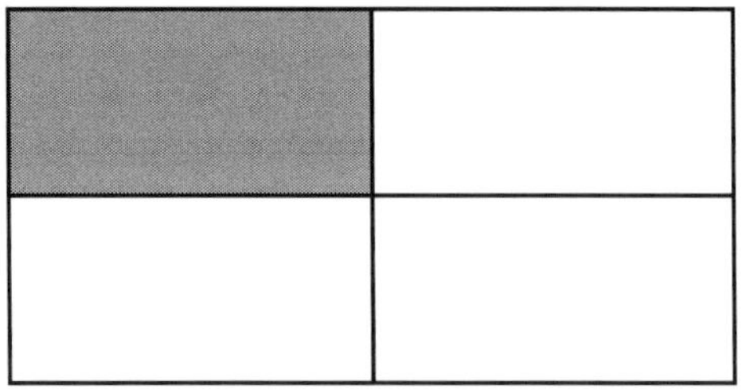

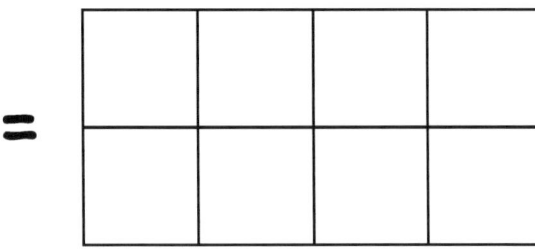

$$\frac{1}{4} = \underline{}$$

2.

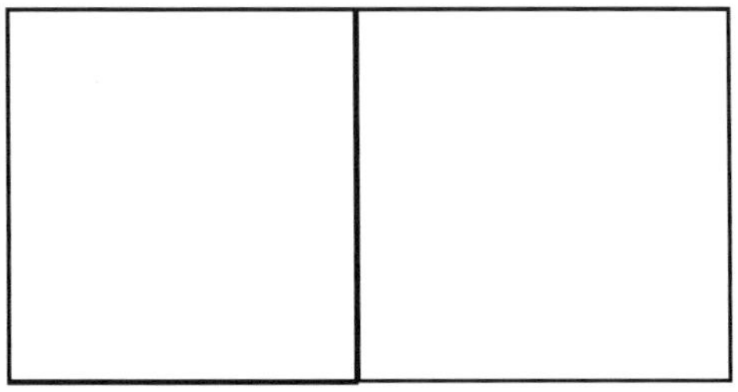

$$\frac{4}{8} = \underline{}$$

175   18.1 Equivalent Fractions

3. $\dfrac{2}{3}$ = $\dfrac{}{}$

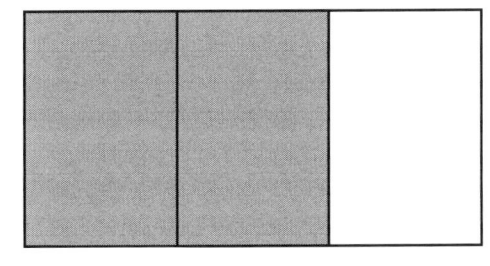

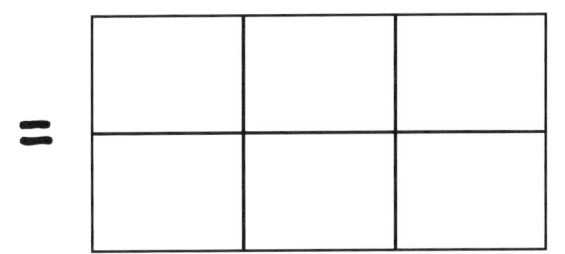

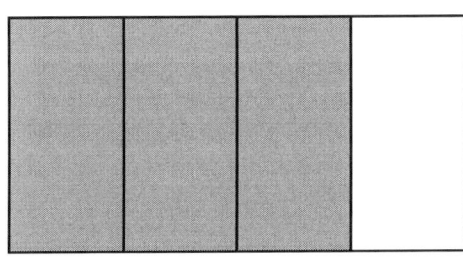

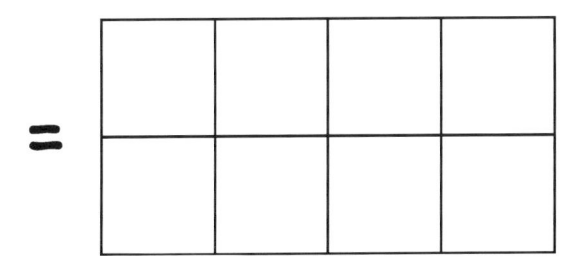

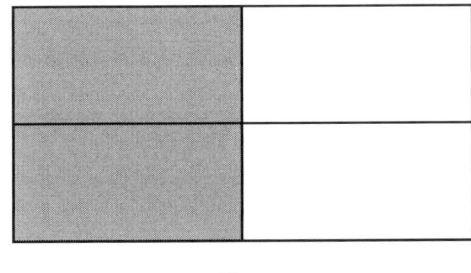

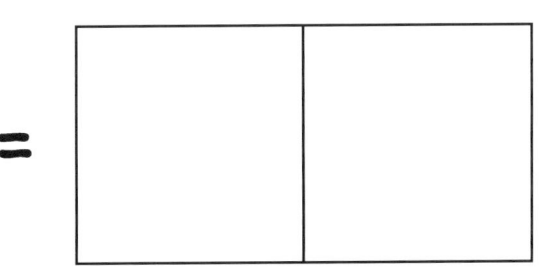

4. $\dfrac{3}{4}$ = $\dfrac{}{}$

5. $\dfrac{2}{4}$ = $\dfrac{}{}$

18.1 Equivalent Fractions

Name: _____ Date: _____

Make Equivalent Toys

Read each word problem, and draw the equivalent fraction in each empty picture. Then write the fraction beside each picture.

1. This trampoline has 4 parts. 2 of the parts are shaded. Make an equivalent fraction using a trampoline with 8 parts.

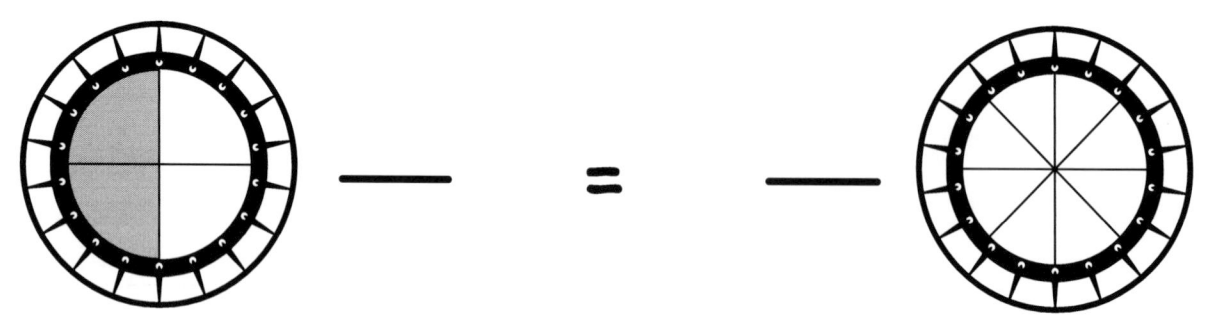

   ___ = ___

2. This slide is half colored in! Make an equivalent fraction on the other slide, using 4 sections instead of 2.

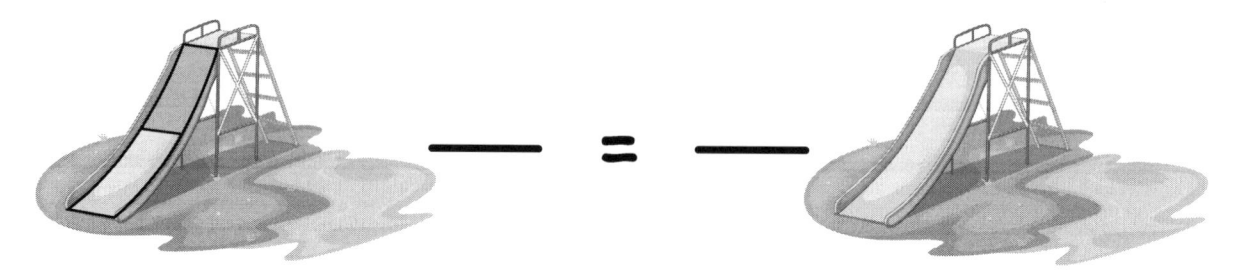

   ___ = ___

3. 4 of the 6 parts of Caleb's toy box are shaded. Make an equivalent fraction using the blank toy box with a total of 3 parts.

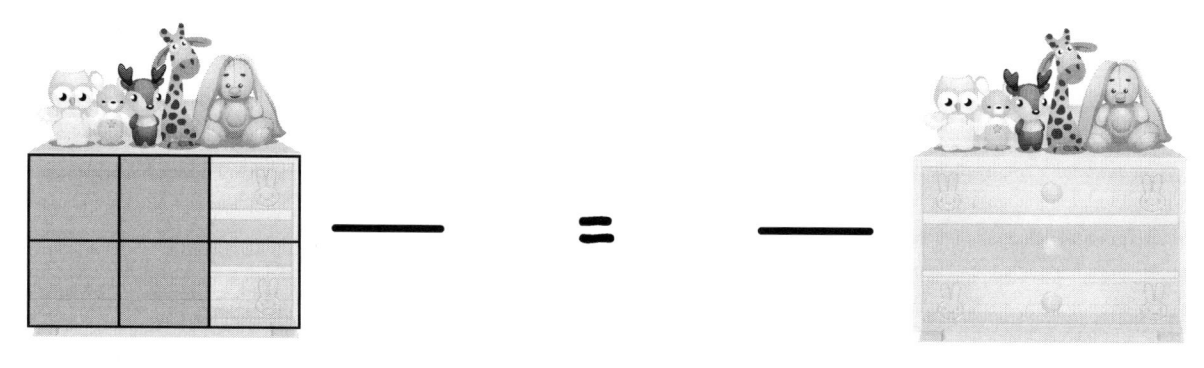

   ___ = ___

177

18.3 Fraction Pie

Next page

4. All 3 parts of this ball are shaded. Create an equivalent fraction with the second ball using a total of 2 parts.

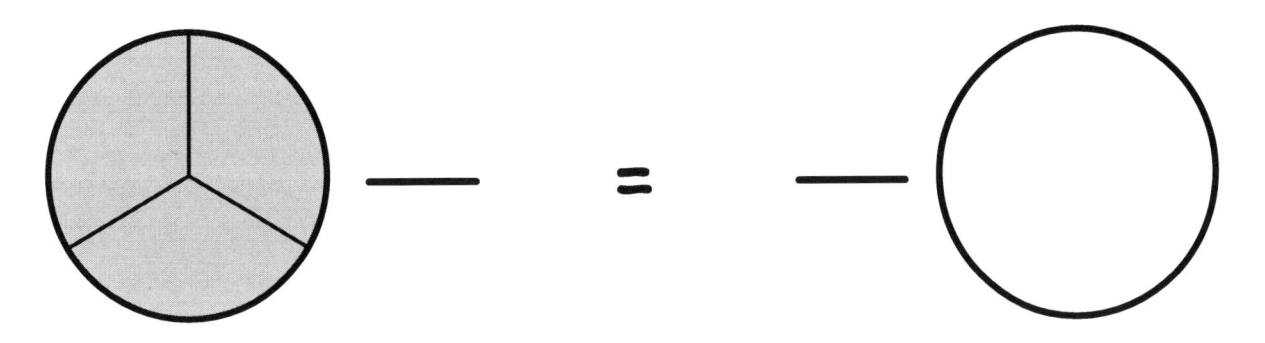

— = —

5. Caleb's block tower has 8 blocks. 4 of the blocks are shaded. Make an equivalent fraction using only 6 blocks.

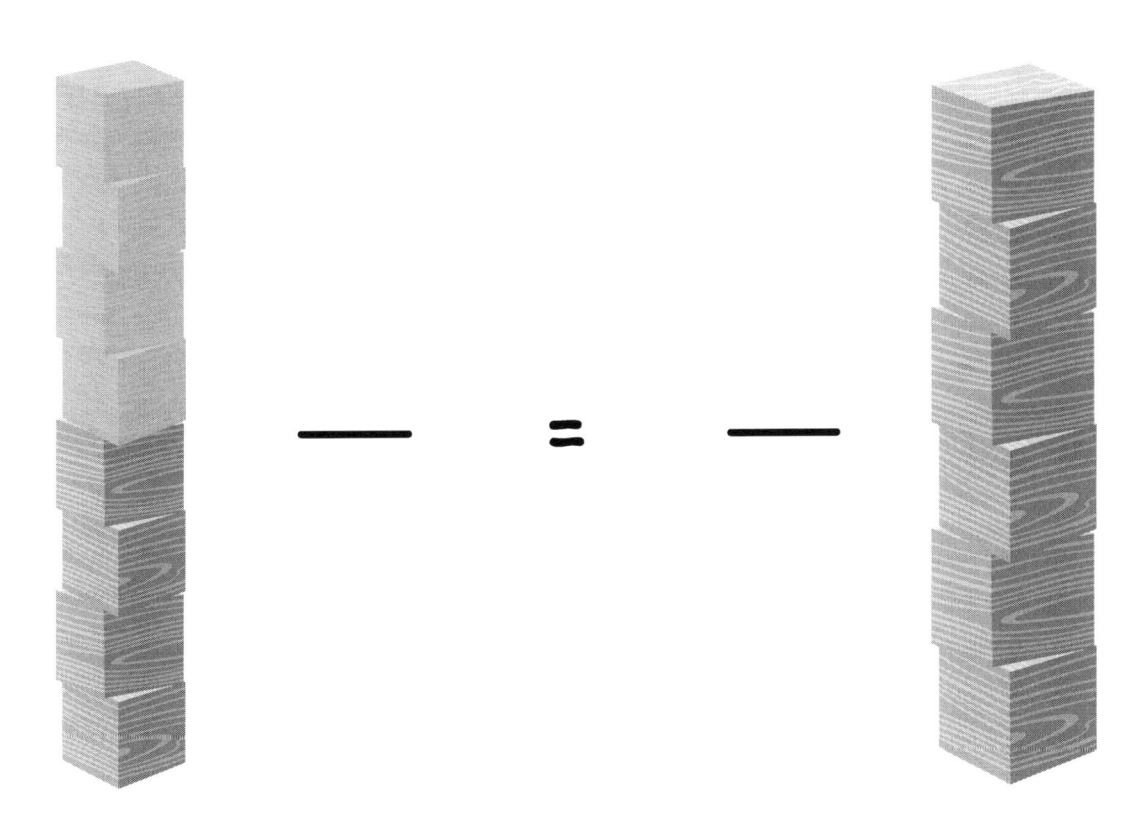

— = —

18.3 Fraction Pie

Name: _____ Date: _____

Create Equivalent Fraction Models

Create shapes and number lines to prove that each pair of fractions below are equivalent. The first one is done for you.

Example:

$$\frac{4}{6} = \frac{2}{3}$$

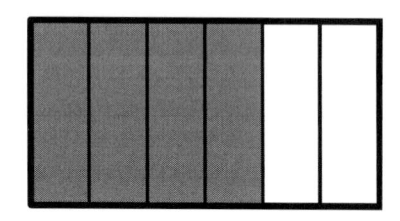

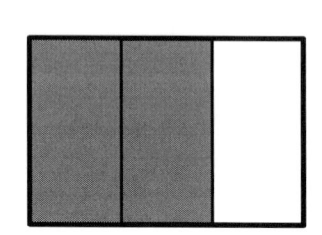

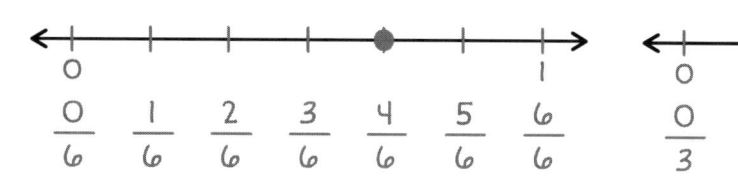

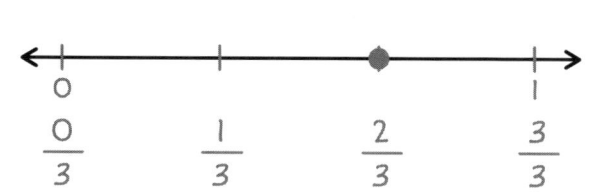

1.

$$\frac{6}{8} = \frac{3}{4}$$

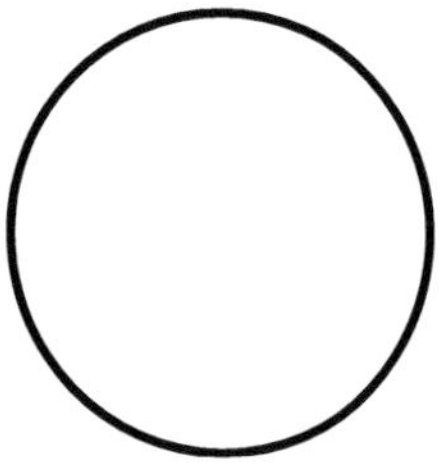

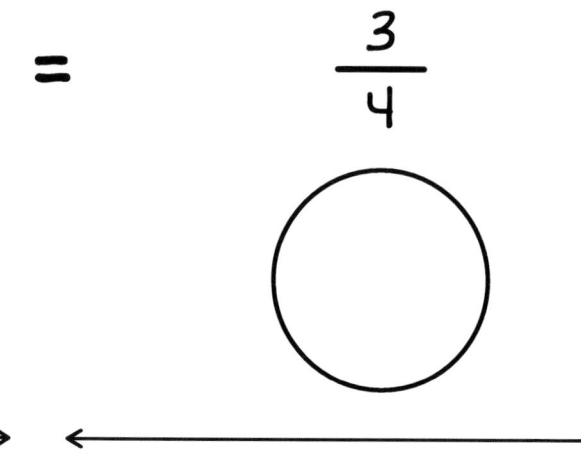

179

18.4 Draw Fractions

Next page

2.

$$\frac{2}{8} = \frac{1}{4}$$

3.

$$\frac{2}{2} = \frac{3}{3}$$

4. What do you notice about the numerators and denominators of the last fractions, $\frac{2}{2}$ and $\frac{3}{3}$? What does it mean when the numerator and denominator are the same?

18.4 Draw Fractions

Name: _____ Date: _____

Find Equivalent Fractions

Find equivalent fractions using number lines and shapes.

1. Logan divided bubbles into 4 containers. He wants to share them with 3 of his friends. Each of them will get 1 container. How many containers will Logan get if he divides the bubbles into 8 containers instead? Label the bottom number line with fractions. Then, write the 2 equivalent fractions.

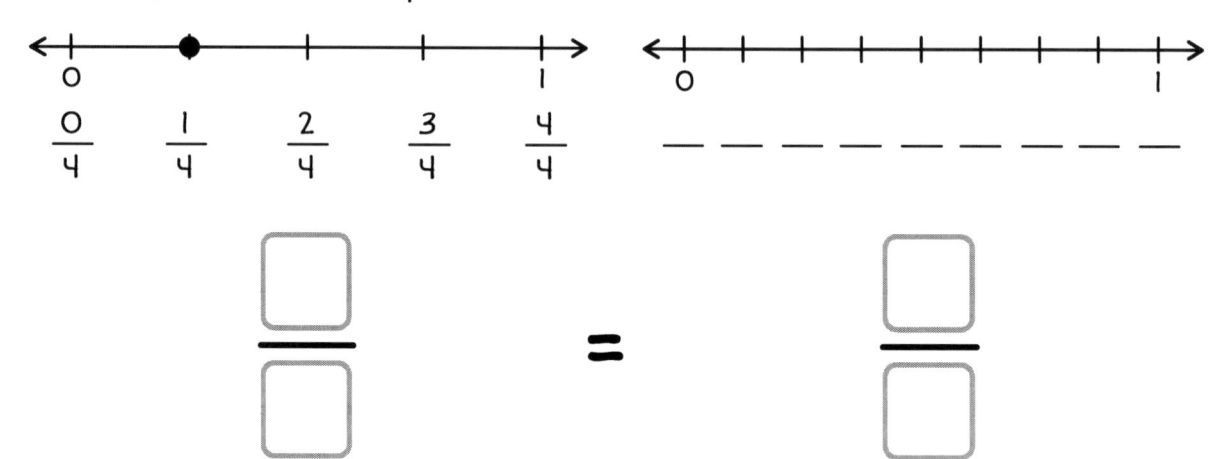

$\frac{0}{4}$ $\frac{1}{4}$ $\frac{2}{4}$ $\frac{3}{4}$ $\frac{4}{4}$

$\dfrac{\Box}{\Box} = \dfrac{\Box}{\Box}$

2. A recipe calls for $\frac{4}{8}$ cup of blueberries. What fraction is equivalent to $\frac{4}{8}$? Color the shapes below. Then, write the equivalent fractions.

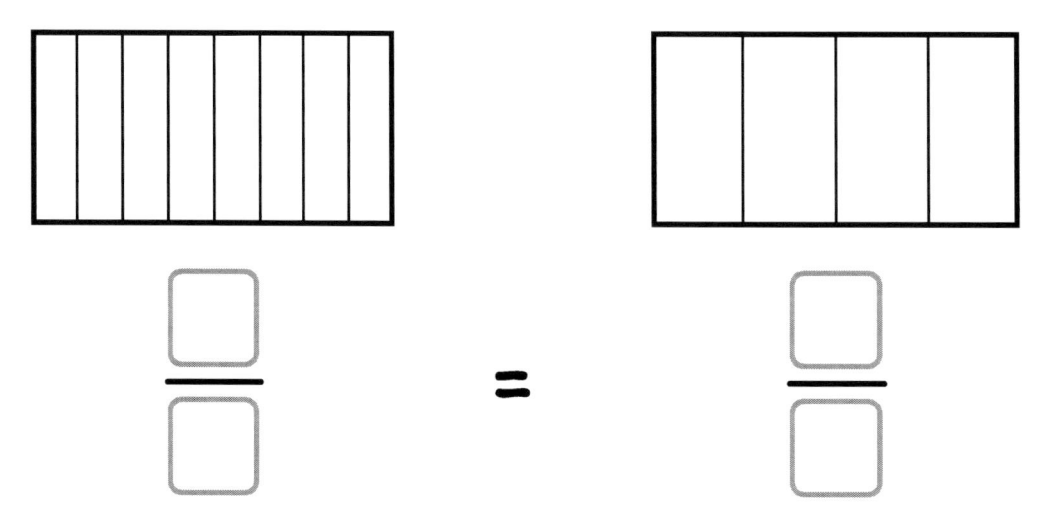

$\dfrac{\Box}{\Box} = \dfrac{\Box}{\Box}$

18.5 Problem Solving with Fractions

Next page

3. What are these equivalent fractions? Read each word problem. Then, complete each model and write the equivalent fractions below.

Logan has 2 baseball bats. The first is divided into 6 equal parts, and 2 of the parts are colored yellow. The other bat is divided into 3 equal parts.

What are these equivalent fractions? Color the second baseball bat, and write the equivalent fractions.

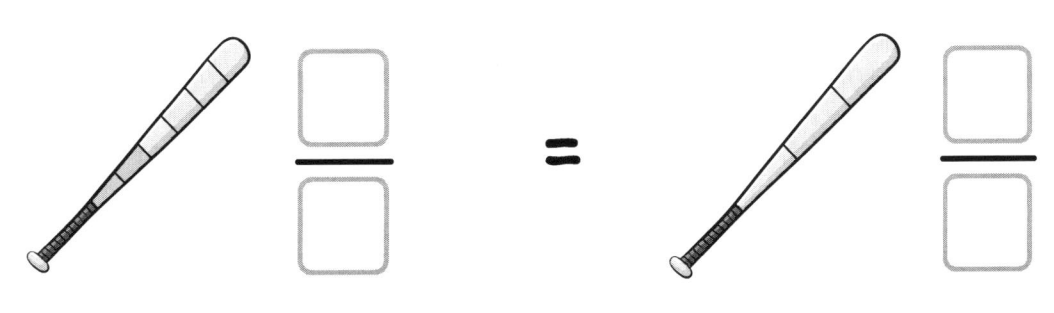

$$\frac{\square}{\square} = \frac{\square}{\square}$$

There are 2 sandwiches on a table. 1 sandwich is cut into 2 equal pieces, and the other is cut into 6 equal pieces. Logan ate half of the first sandwich, and Caleb ate the same amount of the second sandwich.

What are these equivalent fractions? Label each number line below, and record the equivalent fractions using a dot. Then, write the equivalent fractions.

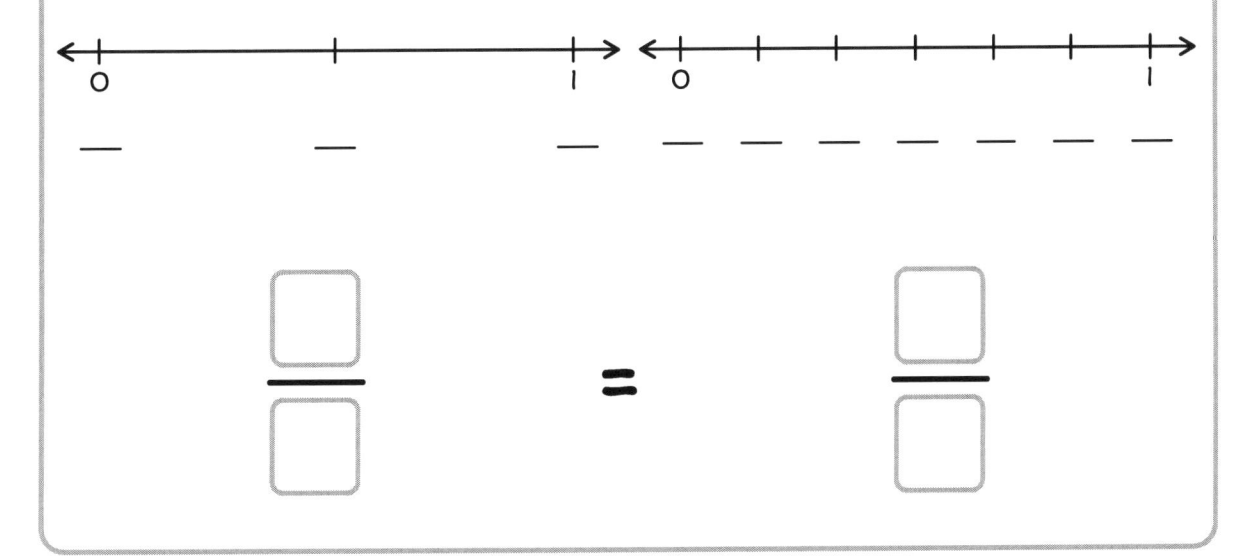

$$\frac{\square}{\square} = \frac{\square}{\square}$$

18.5 Problem Solving with Fractions

This green beach ball has 4 equal parts. Can you color the second beach ball to make an equivalent fraction?

Color the second beach ball, and write the equivalent fractions.

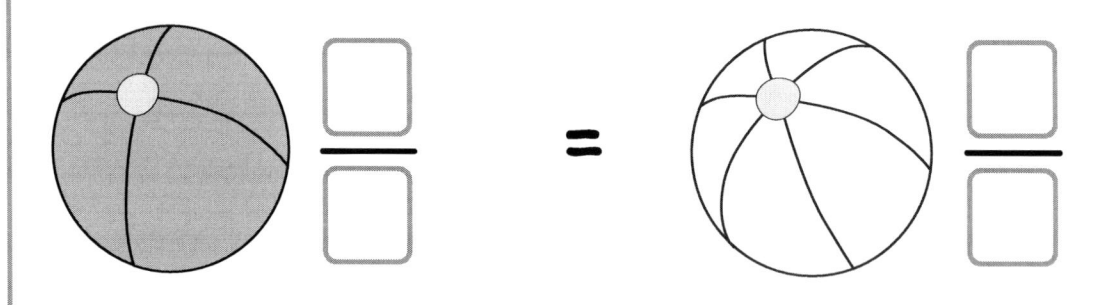

$\dfrac{\square}{\square} = \dfrac{\square}{\square}$

18.5 Problem Solving with Fractions

Cutout Worksheets

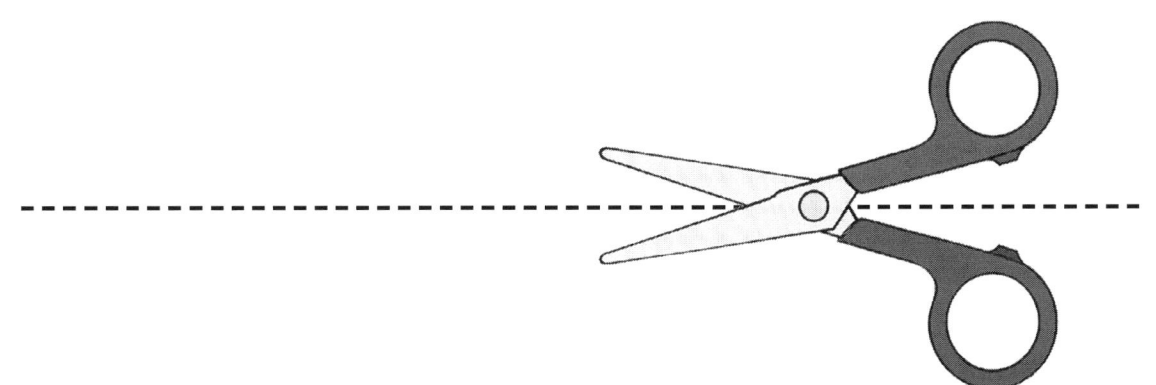

Name: _____ Date: _____

Search and Write!

Use the repeated addition sentence to find the correct skip-counting sequence. Cut it out and glue it in the box. Then write and solve the multiplication sentence.

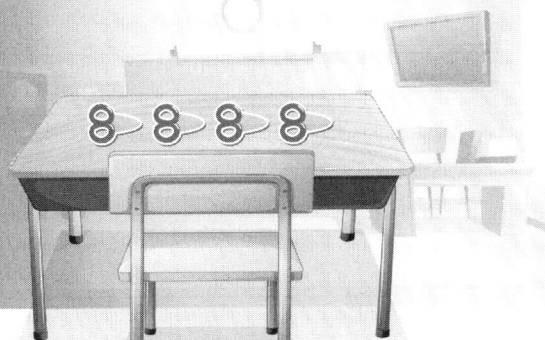

Example:

3,6

3 + 3 = ?

$\underline{2}$ x $\underline{3}$ = $\underline{6}$

1.

2 + 2 + 2 + 2 + 2 = ?

___ x ___ = ___

2.

3 + 3 + 3 + 3 + 3 + 3 = ?

___ x ___ = ___

1.3 Skip Counting

186
Next page

3.

5 + 5 + 5 + 5 + 5 + 5 + 5 = ?

___ X ___ = ___

4.

10 + 10 + 10 + 10 + 10 + 10 + 10 + 10 = ?

___ X ___ = ___

2, 4, 6, 8	10, 20, 30, 40, 50, 60, 70, 80
5, 10, 15, 20, 25	3, 6, 9, 12, 15, 18, 21, 24
10, 20, 30, 40	2, 4, 6, 8, 10
3, 6, 9, 12, 15, 18	5, 10, 15, 20, 25, 30, 35

1.3 Skip Counting

Name: _____ Date: _____

Cut, Draw, Solve!
Use what you know about multiplication pictures to solve the problems.

Read the equation. Cut out the correct number of circles and glue them in the box. Then draw the correct number of shapes in each circle. Use your picture to find the product and write it on the line.

Example: Create a picture to solve. Use ●s.

$$5 \times 5 = 25$$

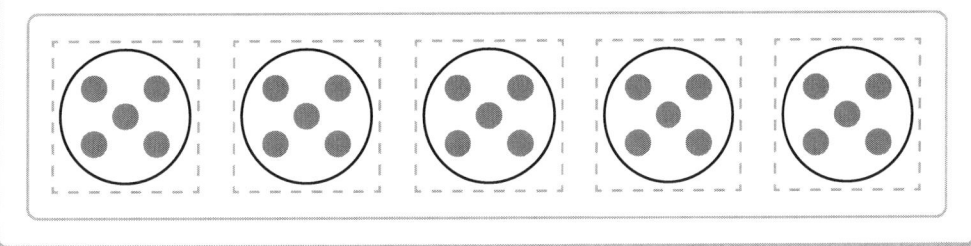

1. Create a picture to solve. Use ■s.

$$9 \times 2 = \_\_\_$$

2.2 Use Pictures to Multiply

190
Next page

2. Create a picture to solve. Use ★s.

$$8 \times 3 = \underline{}$$

3. Create a picture to solve. Use ▬s.

$$7 \times 4 = \underline{}$$

2.2 Use Pictures to Multiply

4. Create a picture to solve. Use ▲s.

$$6 \times 5 = \underline{}$$

2.2 Use Pictures to Multiply

194

Name: _____ Date: _____

Cut, Glue, Solve!
Use what you know about related multiplication and division facts to find the correct pictures.

Cut out the pictures. Glue them in the boxes with the correct math sentences. Then use the pictures to solve!

Example:

$4 \times 3 = \underline{12}$

$12 \div 4 = \underline{3}$

3.3 Relate Multiplication and Division for Groups

196

Next page

1.

$4 \times 4 = \_\_\_$

$16 \div 4 = \_\_\_$

2.

$3 \times 8 = \_\_\_$

$24 \div 3 = \_\_\_$

3.3 Relate Multiplication and Division for Groups

Next page

3.

$9 \times 3 = \underline{}$

$27 \div 9 = \underline{}$

4.

$8 \times 4 = \underline{}$

$32 \div 8 = \underline{}$

3.3 Relate Multiplication and Division for Groups

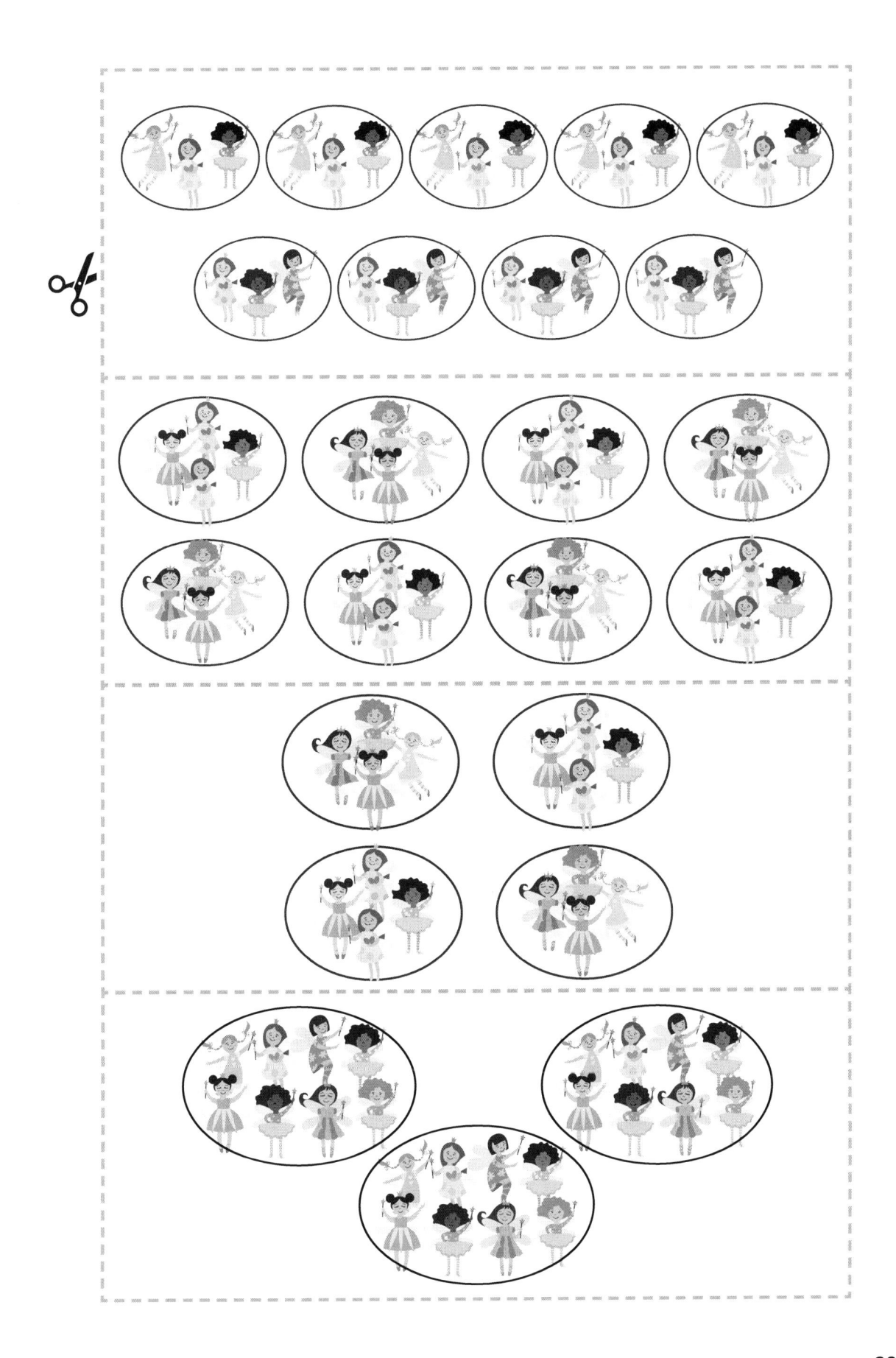

3.3 Relate Multiplication and Division for Groups

200

Name: _____ Date: _____

Compare and Order
Use place value and place-value blocks to compare and order whole numbers.

Can you compare two numbers? Use your place-value blocks to make each number. Then draw the correct symbol in the box to show which number is greater and which number is less.

Example:

36 > 26

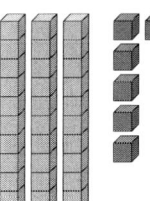

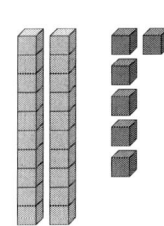

1. 32 ☐ 35

2. 51 ☐ 48

3. 146 ☐ 133

4. 259 ☐ 310

5.1 Compare and Order Numbers

202
Next page

Can you put three numbers in order? Use your place-value blocks to make each number. Then cut out the numbers and glue them in the boxes so they are in the correct order.

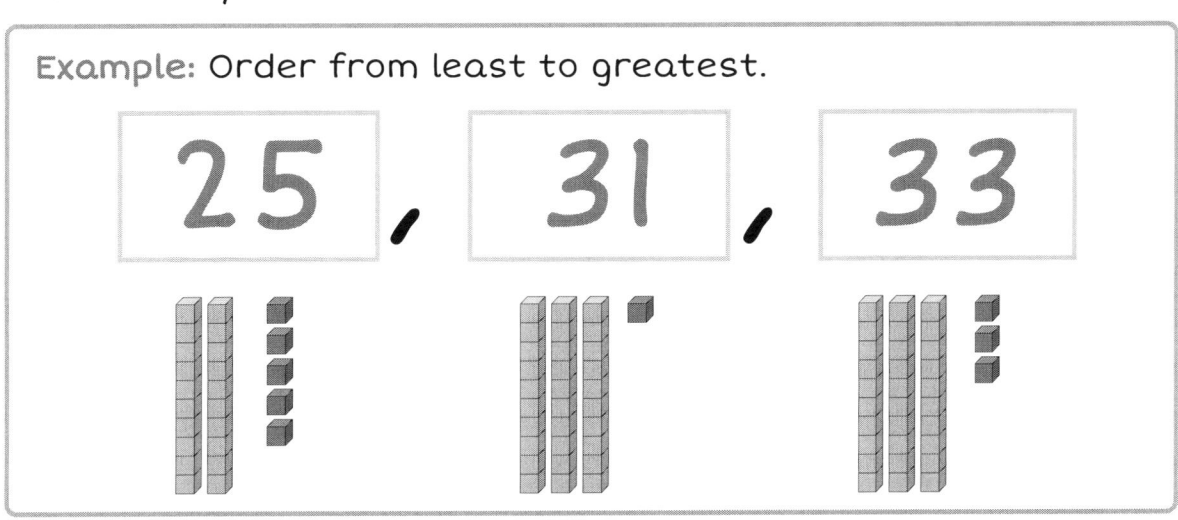

Example: Order from least to greatest.

25 , 31 , 33

1. Put the numbers in order from least to greatest. **102, 111, 85**

2. Put the numbers in order from greatest to least. **125, 101, 133**

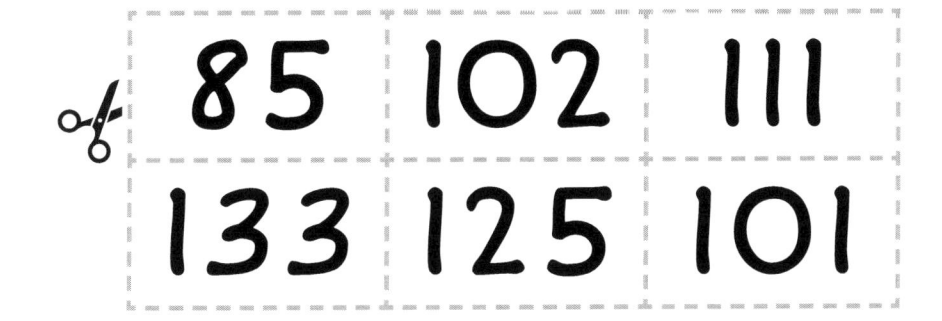

85 102 111
133 125 101

5.1 Compare and Order Numbers

Name: _____ Date: _____

Solve for Unknown Quantities

Find the unknown quantity of an equation to solve a word problem.

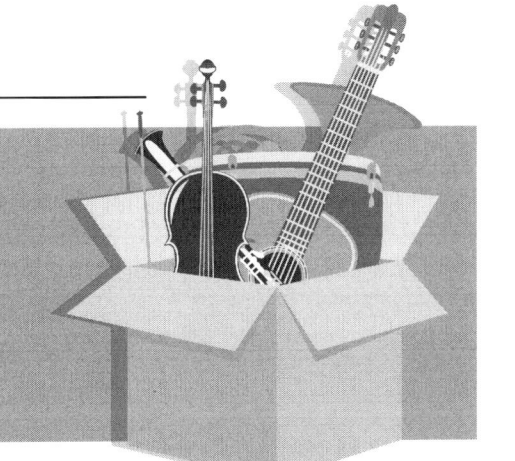

Logan needs your help adding, subtracting, multiplying, or dividing to find the unknown quantity of each instrument. Create the equation. Write the sum, difference, product, or quotient in the box underneath each word problem. Then, write the correct number next to each instrument on Logan's list. You can cut the list out and decorate it to turn in when you are done!

Example:

Logan counts 36 violins. He makes 6 equal groups of violins. How many violins are in each group?

$\underline{36} \div \underline{6} = ?$ $\boxed{6} = ?$

Find the violin on the list and write a 6 on the line in front of it.

1. Logan counts 41 red guitars and 27 yellow guitars. How many guitars does he count in total?

   ___ + ___ = G

   $\boxed{}$ = G

2. Logan has 7 boxes of instruments. There are 5 oboes in each box. How many flutes are there in all?

   ___ × ___ = ?

   $\boxed{}$ = ?

7.1 Represent an Unknown with a Letter or Symbol

3. Logan counts 48 drums. He makes 6 equal groups of drums. How many drums are in each group?

___ ÷ ___ = D

☐ = D

4. Logan counts 55 French horns. 38 of them need to be fixed. How many French horns are left over to play?

___ - ___ = ?

☐ = ?

Logan's Instrument List

6

Name: _____ Date: _____

Is It Reasonable?

Use what you know about reasonable answers to find the sums or differences of math sentences.

Caleb needs to pick the correct instruments to take to the concert! To help him, round each number. Write the digits in the correct boxes. Find the sums or differences of the math sentences for each word problem. Then decide which answers are reasonable, and circle "reasonable" or "unreasonable." Cut out and glue the instruments with the reasonable answers in the boxes on the second page!

Example:

Caleb sees 28 French horns. 13 of them are broken. Is it reasonable to say that there are about 40 French horns left for the class to play?

$$28 - 13 = 15$$

$$30 - 10 = 20$$

If the answer is reasonable, find the instrument with that answer!

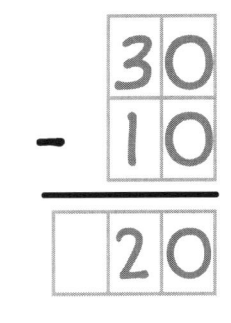

reasonable   (unreasonable)

7.5 Problem Solving: Reasonableness of Answers

210
Next page

1. Caleb finds 61 drums. Then he finds 24 more drums. Is it reasonable to say that Caleb found about 80 drums in all?

$$61 + 24$$

reasonable   unreasonable

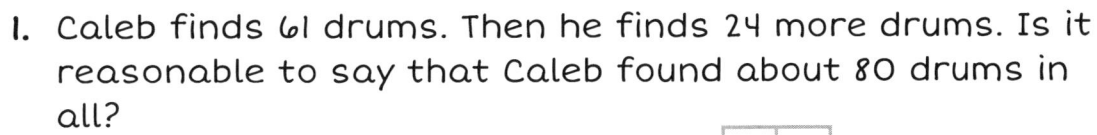

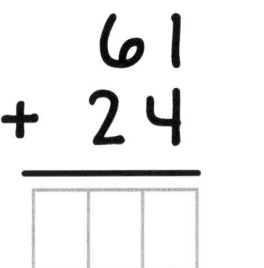

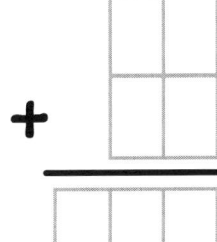

2. Caleb counts 87 French horns. The fourth grade class takes away 52 of them. Is it reasonable to say that there are about 60 French horns left for Caleb's class?

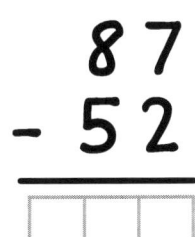

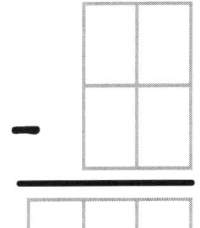

$$87 - 52$$

reasonable   unreasonable

3. Caleb counts 313 red guitars and 88 blue guitars. Is it reasonable to say that Caleb counts about 200 guitars in total?

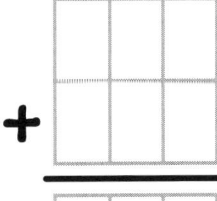

$$313 + 88$$

reasonable   unreasonable

7.5 Problem Solving: Reasonableness of Answers

4. Caleb sees 765 violins. He leaves 593 of them in the music room. Is it reasonable to say that Caleb takes about 200 voilins to the concert?

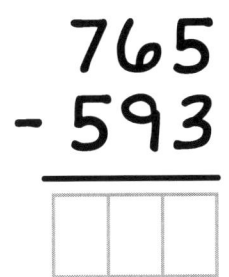

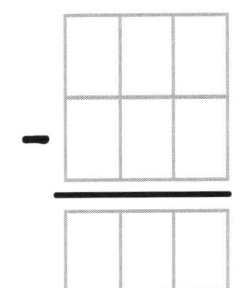

765
- 593

reasonable   unreasonable

80   60   700   200

7.5 Problem Solving: Reasonableness of Answers

Name: _____ Date: _____

Circle, Solve, Make!
Use the properties of operations to solve equations.

Daniel needs your help to make a plate of "ants on a log" snacks! Circle and use one of the properties of operations to solve each equation. Then write the correct answer on the line. Find the snacks with the correct answers. Cut them out and glue them on Daniel's plate.

(identity) commutative associative distributive

73 + 0 = 73

Find the snack that has the number 73 on it. Cut it out and glue it on Daniel's plate!

1. identity commutative associative distributive

16 + 29 = 45

29 + 16 = ☐

2. identity commutative associative distributive

88 + 0 = ☐

3. identity commutative associative distributive

3 × (8 + 2) = ☐

8.2 Properties of Operations

4. identity   commutative   associative   distributive

$$(32 + 15) + 24 = 71$$
$$32 + (15 + 24) = \boxed{}$$

5. identity   commutative   associative   distributive

$$54 + 36 = 90$$
$$36 + 54 = \boxed{}$$

6. Challenge: Multiplication equations use the same properties of operations as addition equations. Which property should you use to solve the equation below? Circle the correct property. Then write or draw to show why you chose that property.

identity   commutative   associative   distributive

$$6 \times 4 = 24 \qquad 4 \times 6 = ?$$

_____

_____

_____

_____

8.2 Properties of Operations

218

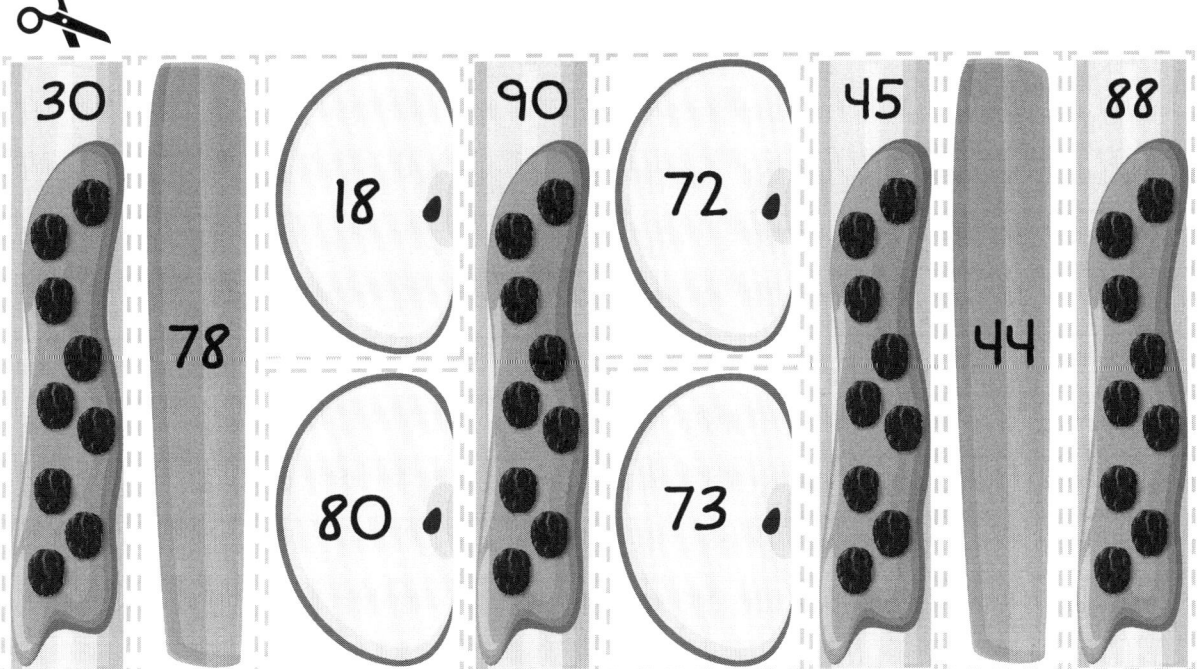

8.2 Properties of Operations

220

Name: _____ Date: _____

Solve and Create
Use the distributive property to solve multiplication sentences.

Madelyn wants to count the empty seats on another Adventure Land ride. Fill in the empty lines for each problem to use the distributive property. Then, write the total product in each box. Look for the picture pieces that have the correct answers on them. Cut them out and glue them together to make a picture of the ride!

Example:

$4 \times 10 = ?$

$4 \times (5 + 5) = ?$

$(4 \times \underline{5}) + (4 \times \underline{5}) = ?$

$\underline{20} + \underline{20} = \boxed{40}$

Look for the picture piece that has a 40 on it!

1.

$3 \times 5 = ?$

$3 \times (2 + 3) = ?$

$(\underline{} \times 2) + (\underline{} \times 3) = ?$

$\underline{} + \underline{} = \boxed{}$

9.2 The Distributive Property of Multiplication

2.

$4 \times 8 = ?$

$4 \times (5 + 3) = ?$

$(4 \times \underline{}) + (4 \times \underline{}) = ?$

$\underline{} + \underline{} = \boxed{}$

3.

$5 \times 9 = ?$

$5 \times (\underline{} + 5) = ?$

$(\underline{} \times 4) + (\underline{} \times 5) = ?$

$\underline{} + \underline{} = \boxed{}$

4.

$6 \times 6 = ?$

$6 \times (3 + \underline{}) = ?$

$(6 \times \underline{}) + (6 \times \underline{}) = ?$

$\underline{} + \underline{} = \boxed{}$

9.2 The Distributive Property of Multiplication

Next page

9.2 The Distributive Property of Multiplication

9.2 The Distributive Property of Multiplication

226

Name: _____ Date: _____

Choose an Operation!

Read each multiplication equation. Decide which operation will help you find the unknown factor or product. Then cut out the multiplication or related division fact and glue it next to the equation.

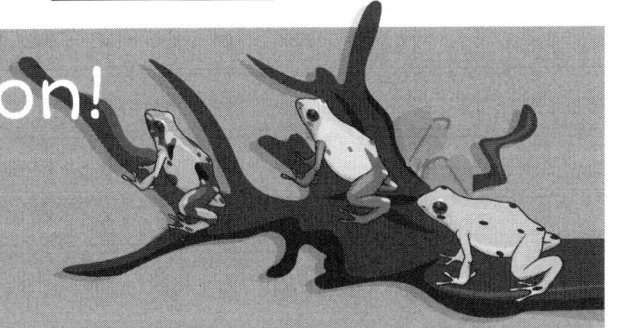

	Multiplication Equation	Related Fact
Example	? x 9 = 54	54 ÷ 9 = ?
	6 x 7 = ?	
	? x 7 = 49	
	8 x ? = 80	
	9 x 7 = ?	
	10 x ? = 80	

✂ | 80 ÷ 10 = ? | ? ÷ 9 = 7 | 49 ÷ 7 = ?

80 ÷ 8 = ? | ? ÷ 6 = 7

10.4 Related Facts: Multiplication and Division

Name: _____ Date: _____

Use the Divisors 1 - 5

1. Write the quotients in the blanks below.

6 ÷ 1 = __6__

100 ÷ 100 = ____

28 ÷ 4 = ____

27 ÷ 3 = ____

9 ÷ 3 = ____

32 ÷ 4 = ____

6 ÷ 2 = ____

12 ÷ 3 = ____

12 ÷ 2 = ____

8 ÷ 4 = ____

20 ÷ 5 = ____

40 ÷ 5 = ____

20 ÷ 2 = ____

7 ÷ 1 = ____

50 ÷ 5 = ____

36 ÷ 4 = ____

2. Prove you know how to use these division strategies! Cut out each strategy on the next page, and glue it under one of the problems below. Find the quotient using the strategy you chose.

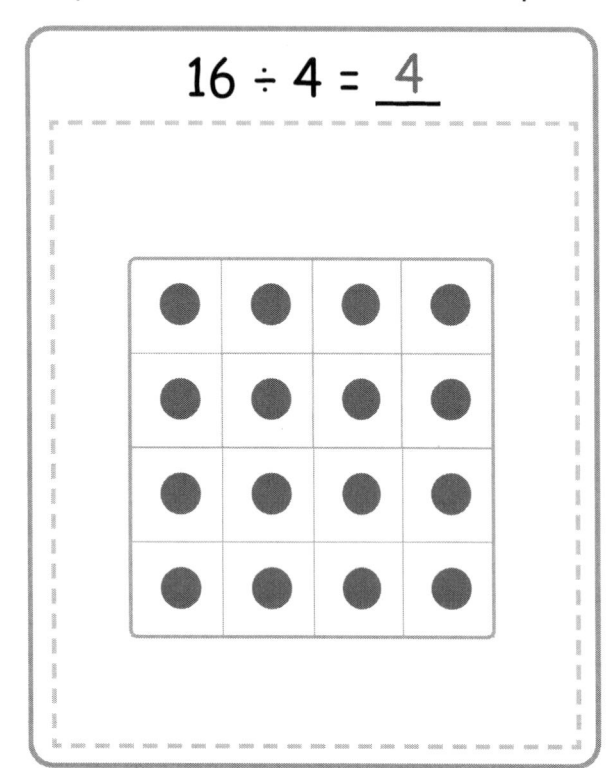

16 ÷ 4 = __4__

10 ÷ 5 = ___

21 ÷ 3 = ___

16 ÷ 2 = ___

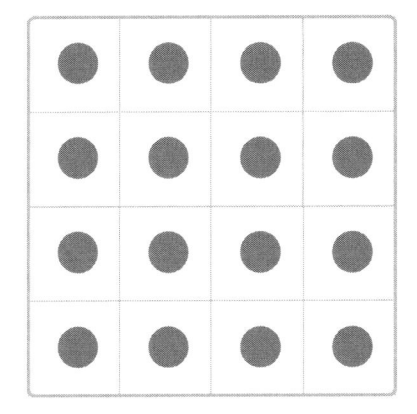

10 − 5 − 5 = 0

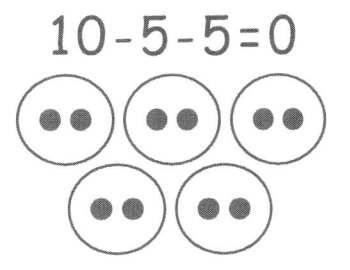

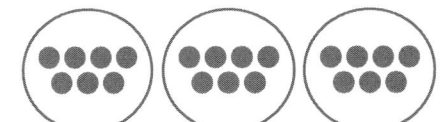

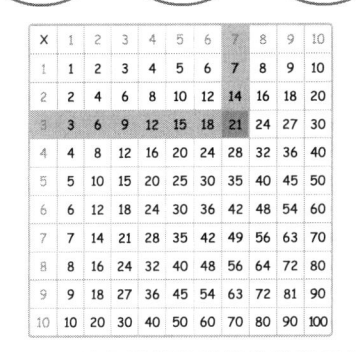

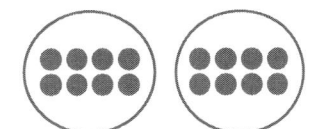

21 − 3 − 3 − 3 − 3 − 3 − 3 − 3 = 0

16 − 2 − 2 − 2 − 2 − 2 − 2 − 2 − 2 = 0

14.4 Division Facts 1 Through 5 Review

Name: _____   Date: _____

Fractions of a Whole

Use what you know about unit fractions to answer the questions.

1.

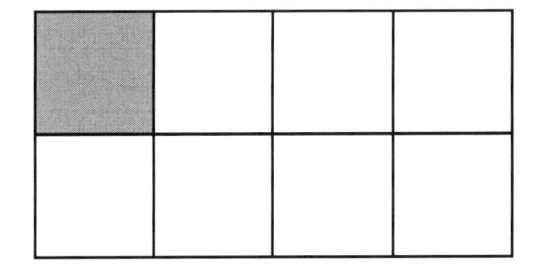

   How many equal parts make up this rectangle? _____

   How many parts are shaded? _____

   What unit fraction describes the shaded part of this rectangle?

   _____

2. Cut out each partitioned circle below. Then, glue it to match its unit fraction.

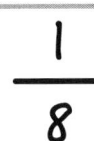

$\frac{1}{4}$	$\frac{1}{3}$	$\frac{1}{8}$	$\frac{1}{6}$	$\frac{1}{2}$

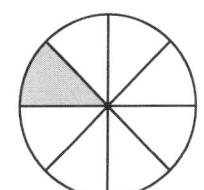

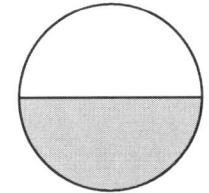

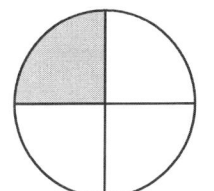

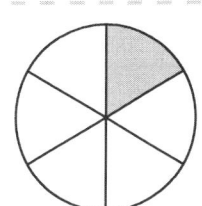

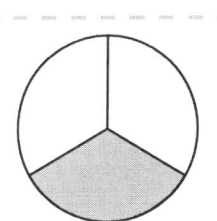

16.1 Unit Fractions

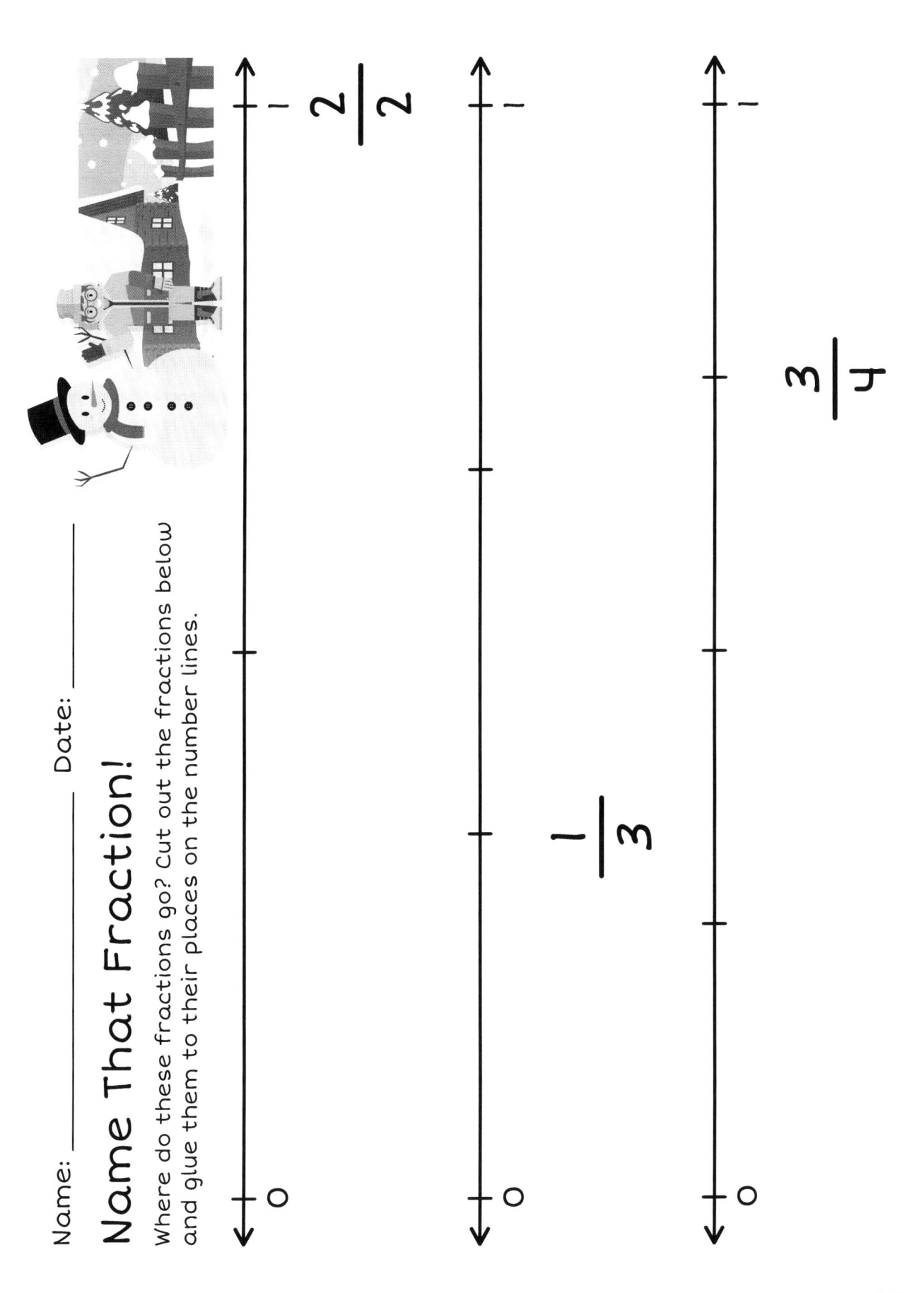

Name: _____   Date: _____

Name That Fraction!

Where do these fractions go? Cut out the fractions below and glue them to their places on the number lines.

$\frac{2}{2}$

$\frac{1}{3}$

$\frac{3}{4}$

17.4 Problem Solve: Reasoning with Fractions

236

$\frac{3}{6}$

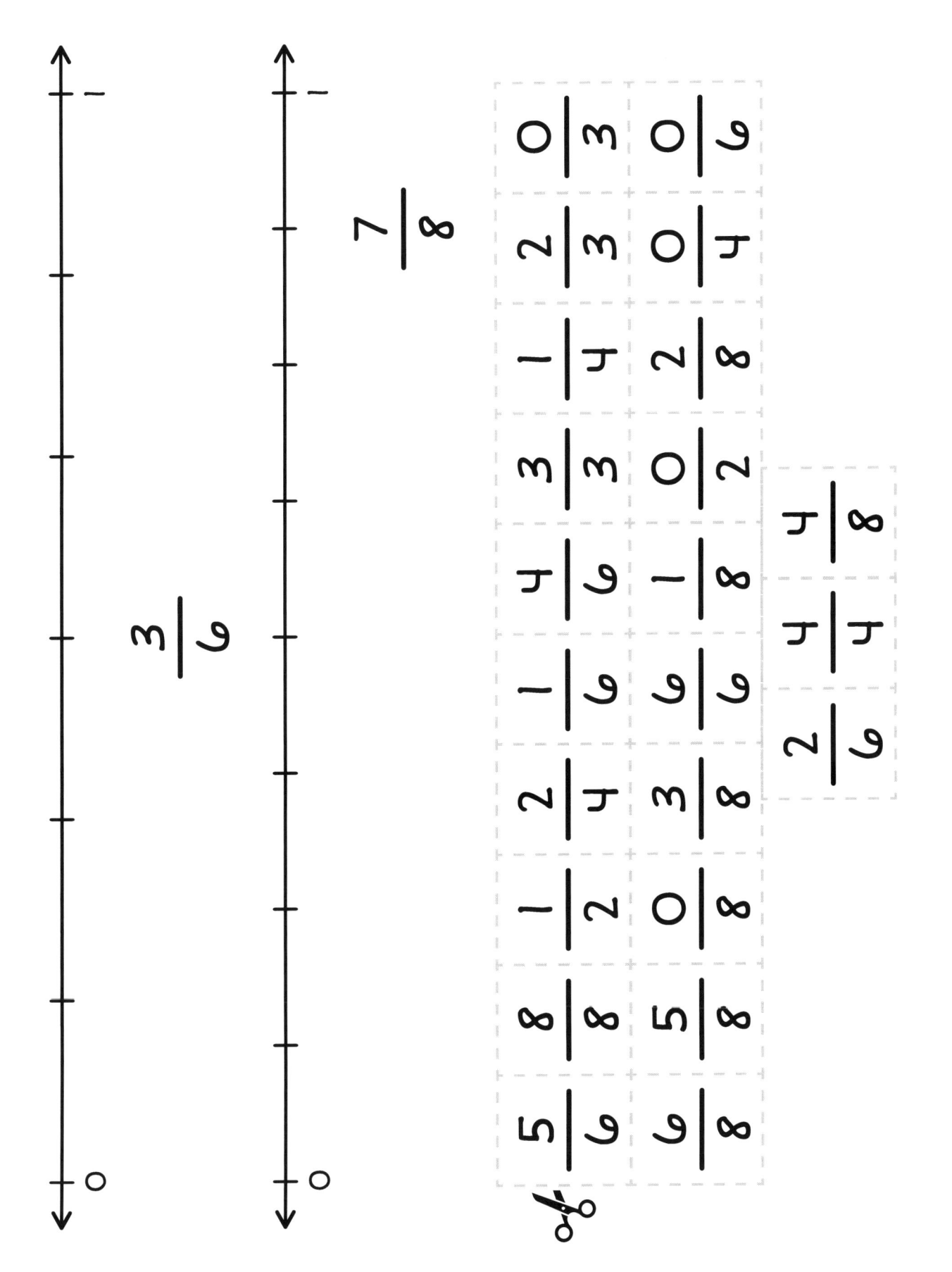

$\frac{7}{8}$

$\frac{5}{6}$	$\frac{8}{8}$	$\frac{1}{2}$	$\frac{2}{4}$	$\frac{1}{6}$	$\frac{4}{6}$	$\frac{3}{3}$	$\frac{1}{4}$	$\frac{2}{3}$	$\frac{0}{3}$
$\frac{6}{8}$	$\frac{5}{8}$	$\frac{0}{8}$	$\frac{3}{8}$	$\frac{6}{6}$	$\frac{1}{8}$	$\frac{0}{2}$	$\frac{2}{8}$	$\frac{0}{4}$	$\frac{0}{6}$

$\frac{2}{6}$	$\frac{2}{4}$	$\frac{4}{8}$

17.4 Problem Solve: Reasoning with Fractions

Name: _____ Date: _____

Create Equivalent Fractions

Cut out the fraction shapes and number lines below. Then, match and glue each fraction shape and number line with its equivalent fraction. Do not forget to fill in the missing numerator or denominator!

Example: $\dfrac{4}{4} = \dfrac{6}{6}$

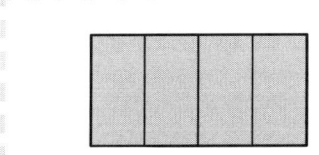

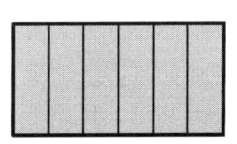

1. $\dfrac{2}{3} = \dfrac{}{6}$

2. $\dfrac{3}{} = \dfrac{6}{8}$

18.2 Find Equivalent Fractions

3. $\dfrac{0}{2}$ = $\dfrac{0}{}$

4. $\dfrac{}{2}$ = $\dfrac{2}{4}$

5. $\dfrac{3}{}$ = $\dfrac{6}{6}$

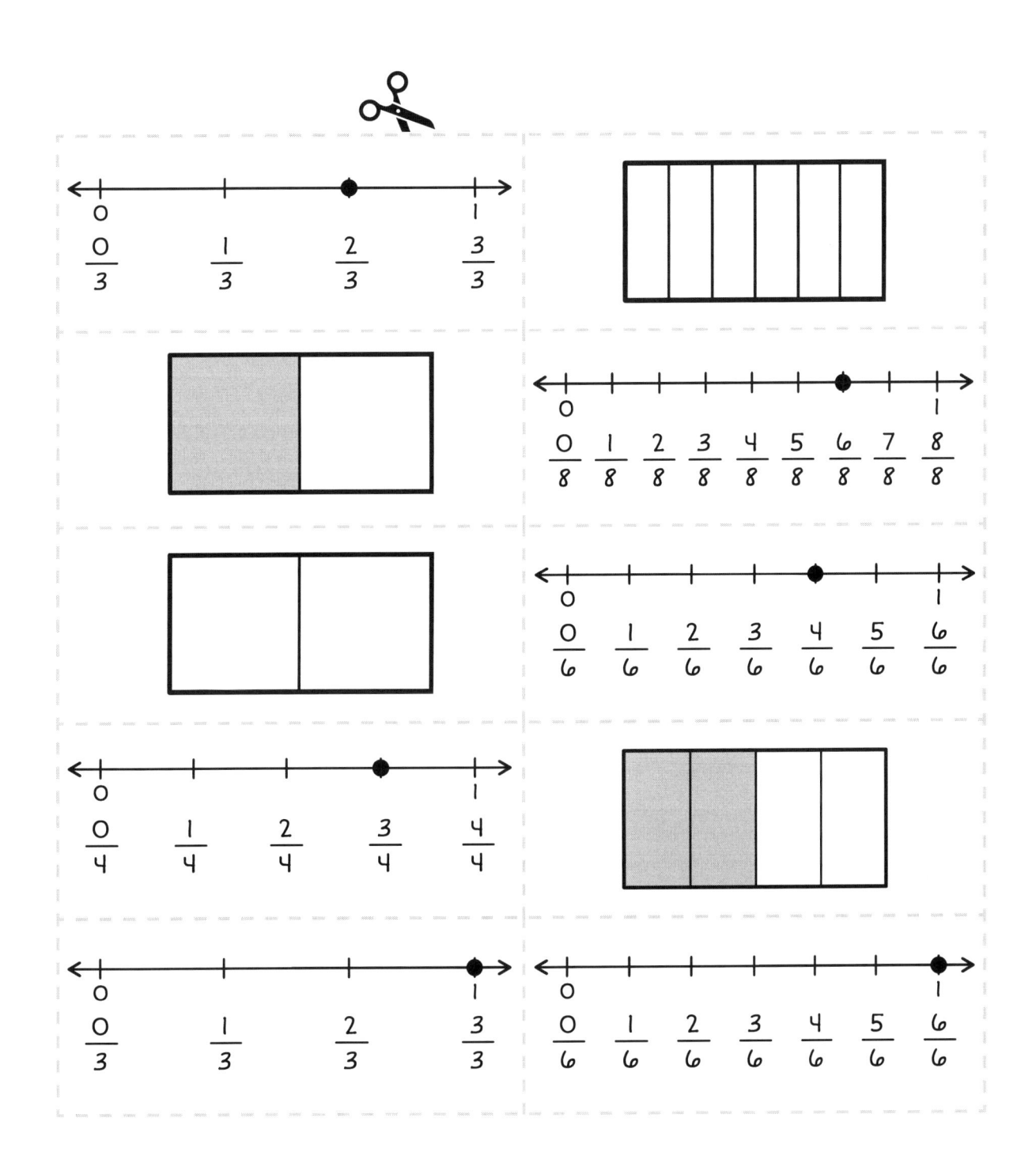

18.2 Find Equivalent Fractions

Extra Resources

The following pages are extra copies of tools you have learned to use in class. They may be helpful as you work through lessons.

Addition Table

+	1	2	3	4	5	6	7	8	9	10
1	2	3	4	5	6	7	8	9	10	11
2	3	4	5	6	7	8	9	10	11	12
3	4	5	6	7	8	9	10	11	12	13
4	5	6	7	8	9	10	11	12	13	14
5	6	7	8	9	10	11	12	13	14	15
6	7	8	9	10	11	12	13	14	15	16
7	8	9	10	11	12	13	14	15	16	17
8	9	10	11	12	13	14	15	16	17	18
9	10	11	12	13	14	15	16	17	18	19
10	11	12	13	14	15	16	17	18	19	20

Addition Table

+	1	2	3	4	5	6	7	8	9	10
1	2	3	4	5	6	7	8	9	10	11
2	3	4	5	6	7	8	9	10	11	12
3	4	5	6	7	8	9	10	11	12	13
4	5	6	7	8	9	10	11	12	13	14
5	6	7	8	9	10	11	12	13	14	15
6	7	8	9	10	11	12	13	14	15	16
7	8	9	10	11	12	13	14	15	16	17
8	9	10	11	12	13	14	15	16	17	18
9	10	11	12	13	14	15	16	17	18	19
10	11	12	13	14	15	16	17	18	19	20

Multiplication Table

X	1	2	3	4	5	6	7	8	9	10
1	1	2	3	4	5	6	7	8	9	10
2	2	4	6	8	10	12	14	16	18	20
3	3	6	9	12	15	18	21	24	27	30
4	4	8	12	16	20	24	28	32	36	40
5	5	10	15	20	25	30	35	40	45	50
6	6	12	18	24	30	36	42	48	54	60
7	7	14	21	28	35	42	49	56	63	70
8	8	16	24	32	40	48	56	64	72	80
9	9	18	27	36	45	54	63	72	81	90
10	10	20	30	40	50	60	70	80	90	100

Multiplication Table

X	1	2	3	4	5	6	7	8	9	10
1	1	2	3	4	5	6	7	8	9	10
2	2	4	6	8	10	12	14	16	18	20
3	3	6	9	12	15	18	21	24	27	30
4	4	8	12	16	20	24	28	32	36	40
5	5	10	15	20	25	30	35	40	45	50
6	6	12	18	24	30	36	42	48	54	60
7	7	14	21	28	35	42	49	56	63	70
8	8	16	24	32	40	48	56	64	72	80
9	9	18	27	36	45	54	63	72	81	90
10	10	20	30	40	50	60	70	80	90	100

Multiplication Table